MINISTRY OF AGRICULTURE, FISHERIES AND FOOD

A D A S

Potato Pests

Reference Book 187

LONDON: HER MAJESTY'S STATIONERY OFFICE

Acknowledgements

Many members of the ADAS Entomology Discipline, past and present, have contributed to the writing of this book, but the main authors of the final text are as follows: the late Mr H. G. Morgan, Mr A. L. Winfield, Mr A. W. Jackson, Mrs C. M. Port, Dr W. E. Parker, Mr R. Gair, Mr J. P. Rogerson, Mr C. R. B. Baker and Mr J. F. Southey. Mr J. S. Gunn, while the National Specialist for Cash Root Crops, helped with the section on crop losses and the benefits of pest control. Dr S. A. Hill, the National Virology Specialist, made constructive suggestions on the virology component of the aphid sections.

In the final co-ordination and technical editing of the text I have been greatly assisted by Mr A. Lane, Chairman of the Arable Crops Entomology Group, and Mrs M. Hancock, Secretary of this Group: without them I might never have fulfilled my promise to the Entomology Discipline of getting this book published before my retirement.

M. Gratwick
Editor

Illustrations

Figures were drawn by the following ADAS Entomologists:

Mr L. R. Wardlow — 1a, 1b, 2a, 2b, 3, 4, 5, 6, 7, 8, 9, 10, 11, 12, 13, 14, 17b, 18b, 20b
Mr J. J. Williams — 15a, 15b, 16a, 16b, 17a, 18a, 19a, 19b, 20a
Miss R. M. Ayres — 22
Dr J. Cotten revised the distribution map in Fig. 21

Photographs (Crown copyright) have been reproduced from slides in the following ADAS Entomology or Plant Pathology, National or Departmental, Collections:

Entomology	Plate No.	Plant Pathology	Plate No.
National Collection	1c, 2c, 3c, 5c, 6a, 6b, 6d, 8a, 8c	National Collection	4d
Harpenden Laboratory	1b, 3d, 4a, 4b, 4c, 5b, 8b	Reading	2b
Aberystwyth	1a, 6c		
Bristol	3b		
Cambridge	2a, 2d, 3a, 7c		
Kirton	7a		
Reading	7b, 7d		
Wye	5a		

Contents

Foreword

The potato crop is a major component of many rotations on arable farms; 130 000 hectares of the crop were grown in 1987 with a value of about £500 million. The seed crop is also important in some areas of the UK.

Production of ware and seed crops tends to be concentrated on fewer, more specialised farms, often on the lighter soils. The resulting intensive cropping regimes, together with an increasing demand for healthy seed and high quality tubers for the processing industry, increase the need for effective pest control and require a better understanding of the biology of the pests.

This new publication provides a comprehensive reference book to the major and less common pests of the crop and will be a useful guide for those concerned with crop protection problems on potatoes. The introduction outlines the history and development of potato cropping in the British Isles, giving examples of the way native pests have become adapted to the introduced potato plant. It also discusses the establishment here of non-indigenous pests, such as potato cyst nematode associated with the crop in South America. Estimates are given of losses caused by the major pests together with information on the use of pesticides on the crop.

Detailed descriptions are given of each pest, its biology and symptoms of damage. The reader is helped to identify the problem by means of a comprehensive damage symptom key, with detailed line drawings and colour plates of the major pests and the damage they cause. Where control measures are necessary, recommendations are included.

Potato cyst nematode is still the major pest of the ware crop and this is discussed in detail, including reference to the development of integrated control strategies based on rotations, resistant varieties and nematicides. The problem of pesticide resistance in the important virus vector the peach–potato aphid is also fully discussed.

Special thanks are due to Miss Marion Gratwick for her untiring efforts in drawing together the many contributions to this new publication. She has acknowledged elsewhere the help of colleagues in the Entomology Discipline past and present.

H. J. Gould
Director, Harpenden Laboratory
October 1987

Introduction

History of potato cropping in the British Isles

The potato is now one of the major food plants of Europe, but it is not native to this continent. It was first introduced from South America in the second half of the 16th century and is recorded as being grown in a private garden in London in 1596. At first it was regarded mainly as a curiosity and there was little indication of its future role in the British Isles or the rest of Europe. At the time of its introduction, England was self-sufficient in cereals and remained so for another two hundred years. There was no incentive to cultivate the potato and it was unsuited to the open-field system of farming practised in eastern England. Wales, also, was self-supporting. In Ireland, however, the situation was quite different. The peasants were on the verge of starvation as a result of frequent loss of their cattle and crops during a long period of warfare. Much of the land was subdivided and enclosed and the potato produced more food per acre than any crop currently grown. Potato cultivation therefore spread rapidly throughout Ireland in the first part of the 17th century. During the rebellion in the 1640s, potatoes left in the ground were saved from destruction and so became an increasingly important source of food for the peasants. Eventually the Irish economy became dependent on the potato crop. Hence the crop failures of 1845 and 1846, caused by blight, were disastrous for both the economy and the population — a million people died and during the following six years more than a million emigrated.

The potato was introduced into Scotland from Ireland towards the end of the 17th century and, by 1800, had become an invaluable food crop in the Highlands. The cultivation of the potato as a common foodstuff also spread from Ireland into Wales and northern England during the 17th century. Lancashire was the first English county in which potatoes were grown as a crop. The spread of cultivation to the rest of the country was slow until aided by land enclosures and the Industrial Revolution; the latter led to an increase in population so that English cereal production became inadequate. By the 1790s potato cultivation was extensive in the whole of the west of England and in areas within easy reach of London. Although large-scale cultivation was still not common in some eastern counties, there was an increasing tendency for farm labourers to grow potatoes as an essential foodstuff. This trend was probably furthered by the economic depression that followed the Napoleonic Wars.

During the 19th century the area cropped with potatoes in England and Wales increased, reaching about 142 000 hectares (350 000 acres) in 1866. From then until about 1925 there was a remarkably steady rise of about 900 hectares (2250 acres) per annum, levelling out at just under 200 000 hectares (500 000 acres). This pattern was only interrupted by the two World Wars: in 1914–18 there was a 30 per cent increase over the 'base acreage' and in 1939–45, at the peak of production, a 100 per cent increase. The steady rise in the 'base acreage' was largely due to the expansion of large-scale growing in the eastern counties: virtually the whole of the increase in cropping area between 1882 and 1950 was accounted for by the increased areas in only two counties — Lincolnshire and the Isle of Ely. The wartime increases were

1

achieved partly by the growing of potatoes on land which was unsuitable, by virtue of its climate and soil, and partly by overcropping and the abandonment of the traditional rotations in the eastern counties.

Pest problems

It is against the background of this history that we consider the pest problems of the potato crop in Britain. Since the potato is not a native plant, it had no native pests adapted to it when first grown here. Only one other major crop — the tomato (an even more recent introduction) — is botanically related to the potato, while wild plants belonging to the potato family (Solanaceae) are few and sometimes locally distributed. Thus the pests which have become established on the potato crop during the last two centuries form a miscellaneous and rather incoherent group; they can be divided roughly into three categories as follows.

1. Polyphagous native pests which have been able without difficulty to extend their host range to include the potato wherever it is grown within their reach. These include wireworms, slugs and the peach–potato aphid.

2. Other organisms with more restricted host ranges which have been able to adapt to the potato. Examples are the potato tuber nematode, the bulb and potato aphid and the potato flea beetle. Their success may be judged by the fact that all their common names include 'potato' although this was not their original host.

3. Pests which were adapted to the potato in America and which are capable of surviving in Britain. These may reach this country in the course of international trade and travel. The potato cyst nematodes are already firmly established. Others, like the Colorado beetle, pose a constant threat; there may be others whose potential is still unrealised.

The potato crop is seriously at risk from pest and disease attacks: the Irish potato famine provided an extreme warning of the sort of catastrophe which can occur. When potatoes are grown as part of a mixed farming rotation the risks are minimised, but monoculture, whether on a small or large scale, increases the danger. Potato cyst nematodes illustrate this point. In private gardens and allotments, the potato has often been the only vegetable grown to any extent and there are few established allotment sites which are free from these nematodes. At the other end of the scale, the vast cropping areas in the eastern counties are nowadays cultivated mainly by specialist growers who are unable or unwilling to diversify their cropping. It is here, where economic expediency overrides good agricultural practice, that nematode attack is most concentrated. The situation was aggravated by the overcropping of the war years.

Types of pest damage

Potato pests interact with other factors to affect the value of the crop in various ways: they may decrease the yield or the marketability of the saleable ware crop or they may reduce or destroy the value of the tubers for propagation as 'seed'.

Pests which decrease yield may act at various stages in the life of the crop. Aphid attack during the previous year may lead to virus infection, reducing vigour and tuber production.

Aphid attack in the chitting house, by killing or stunting the developing sprouts, can delay emergence and reduce vigour, and may spread viruses. Damage to the tubers or developing shoots can lead to missing plants or delayed emergence; wireworms, cockchafers, cutworms and symphylids are among the pests which may attack at this stage. Their attacks may persist into the season of foliage growth, when they are joined by several minor leaf- and stem-feeding pests, for example the potato flea beetle and caterpillars such as those of the death's head hawk moth and the rosy rustic moth. It is at this stage that the Colorado beetle, if it ever became established, would exert its effect.

During the full foliage period, sucking insects, such as aphids and leafhoppers, reduce the vigour of the crop. They may do this directly by removal of sap and some of them, such as capsid bugs, also inject toxic saliva. Attacks by sucking pests on the foliage may render the plant more susceptible to attack by other organisms: there is evidence that the control of aphids may delay the onset of potato blight, presumably because the lesions caused by the aphids provide points of entry for the germinating blight spores. Aphids and other sucking pests also act as vectors of viruses. Root-feeding organisms, by interfering with the uptake of nutrients and water, may also reduce vigour at this stage. Both cyst-forming and root-lesion nematodes act in this way, as well as symphylids.

Tuber-feeding organisms cause a negligible loss in the weight of the crop but can render much of it unsaleable. Thus an average of three penetrating wireworm holes per tuber, occupying only a very small percentage of the total volume, would render the whole crop unattractive to the housewife (especially in these days of supermarket sales of washed tubers in transparent bags) and unacceptable to the majority of processors. Wireworms, slugs, millepedes and vertebrate pests such as rodents and birds can all do this type of damage, which often increases markedly after the tubers are mature. The potato tuber moth (see page 95), which can sometimes be found in imported tubers, also reduces marketability in this way.

The main cause of rejection of the crop for seed purposes is virus infection, the control of which necessitates control of the aphid or nematode vectors. The presence of potato cyst nematode in a field also disqualifies the crop for classification for seed purposes. Although nematode cysts are seldom attached to the tubers, they may be present in adhering soil or in the trash in the bags. The planting of contaminated seed was the major cause of the initial spread of potato cyst nematodes in Britain, but nowadays spread is mainly by movement of infested soil on farm equipment etc.

Further reading

ANON. (1972). Potatoes. (5th edition). *Bulletin of the Ministry of Agriculture, Fisheries and Food, London*, No. 94. HMSO.

BURTON, W. G. (1966). *The Potato. A Survey of its History and of Factors Influencing its Yield, Nutritive Value, Quality and Storage.* (2nd edition). Wageningen: H. Veenman & Zonen N. V.

COX, A. E. (1967). *The Potato. A Practical and Scientific Guide.* London: W. H. & L. Collingridge Ltd.

HARRIS, P. M. (Ed.) (1978). *The Potato Crop. The Scientific Basis for Improvement.* London: Chapman & Hall.

McINTOSH, T. P. (1927). *The Potato. Its History, Varieties, Culture and Diseases.* Edinburgh: Oliver and Boyd.

SALAMAN, R. N. (1949). *The History and Social Influence of the Potato.* Cambridge: The University Press.

WHITEHEAD, T., McINTOSH, T. P. and FINDLAY, W. M. (1953). *The Potato in Health and Disease.* (3rd edition). Edinburgh: Oliver and Boyd.

Detection and identification of pest damage

Before control measures can be undertaken, the cause of damage must be established. This may be easy, as when an organism is visible and is clearly doing the damage. On other occasions, the organism may not be seen, either because it is microscopic and therefore invisible to the naked eye or because it has left the plant after causing the damage. It is then necessary to consider the symptoms to obtain a clue to the culprit; other observations may be available to confirm the diagnosis.

Two general points should be made: first, early diagnosis gives the best chance of effective control, so that slight symptoms should not be ignored; secondly, it must be borne in mind that the effects of pest damage may not differ greatly from symptoms due to other causes.

Distribution of damage

It is not only the symptoms on the individual plant that should be considered; their distribution in space and time can also assist in tracking down the causes of trouble. Damage is seldom uniform across a field; if it is, some soil or climatic factor is implied. Sometimes, the damage appears on occasional plants scattered through the crop; this type of distribution suggests attack by a fairly large organism that is present in relatively small numbers.

The commonest pattern of attack is probably the appearance of damage in patches; these patches may spread or they may remain localised in the same area. A spreading patch suggests an organism moving out from an original focus of attack, either because individuals are wandering away from, for example, a single batch of eggs from which they all originated, or because they breed fairly rapidly, with each new generation moving further from the original point of introduction. Aphids spread in this way within a crop and so, on a longer time-scale, do potato cyst nematodes, though with the latter pests the patch is seen to spread from year to year rather than within a single season. Static patches suggest some factor in the soil; this may of course be purely physical or chemical, for example waterlogging, mineral deficiency, or the presence of a localised patch of toxic waste. Nevertheless, pest attack may be related to localised differences in soil conditions: slug damage may be confined to an area of poor drainage or heavier soil, and stubby-root nematodes to a patch of lighter soil.

Another pattern that is sometimes seen in potato crops is the appearance of symptoms along a single row, with an abrupt transition from affected to healthy plants at each end. This suggests some adverse factor affecting a single bag of seed, which may have come from a different source or perhaps have been stored alongside a boiler or some other cause of damage or deterioration.

Damage may appear only along the headlands, suggesting some cause that originated outside the crop. For example, capsid bugs and rodents migrate in from the hedges, and herbicide drift from operations on an adjoining crop may extend only a short distance from the margin of the crop.

Sometimes a clear line of demarcation is seen across a field, with the symptoms confined to one side of the line. If the line does not follow the rows of planting of the crop but cuts across them, the difference should be sought in the past history of the field. Perhaps the cropping of the two parts has been different, for example one part may have been in grass, encouraging wireworms, or in potatoes, encouraging the build-up of cyst nematodes or some other pest specific to potatoes. If the line of demarcation follows the potato rows, the same factors may be involved, but there may be some additional factor related to the origin or treatment of the current crop. The most obvious suggestion is a difference in the source or treatment of the seed, but it is possible that planting, or some later operation, on part of the field took place when the soil was not in a fit condition for working, either causing direct injury or predisposing the plants in that area to pest attack.

The time of development of symptoms may give useful information. For example, damage to the foliage by hail will have occurred at one time and, therefore, at the same stage of development throughout the field; damage by leaf-feeding insects, on the other hand, will occur at different stages on different plants.

Thus, in looking at damage in the field, a great deal of information can be gained by taking a broad view of the development of symptoms. One can compare 'good' with 'bad' plants and so gain a clearer idea of the exact symptoms. In patchy crops one may compare plants from inside the patch with those outside, but more important, in searching for the culprit one should look at the margins of the patch where the damage is actually occurring. In the centre of the patch the damage may be more obvious, but the responsible organism may have left the plants, and secondary organisms, feeding on damaged tissues but not the cause of the original damage, may be present to confuse the issue.

Damage symptoms

It is often difficult to identify the cause of damage from the symptoms alone because many pests produce very similar effects and a wide range of symptoms may be produced by a single species of pest.

The following list, arranged according to the stage of growth of the plants, includes most of the main symptoms and their possible causes.

Symptoms	Causes

Damage before or at emergence

1. Failure to sprout when planted:

    a. Tubers firm — Adverse storage conditions, e.g. overheating or chilling or misuse of sprout suppressant
Potato tuber nematode
Fungus disease

    b. Tubers rotting — Potato tuber nematode
Blight
Fungal storage rots

2. Tubers sprouted but emergence poor:

    a. Sprouts healthy — Cold or dry soil
Physiologically retarded tubers

    b. Sprouts yellowing, brown or wilting — Aphid attack in chitting house

    c. Sprouts brown or blackened at tips — Frost
Pesticide residue in soil

    d. Sprouts partly eaten —
       cut through cleanly — Caterpillar of garden dart moth
Leatherjackets
       with jagged edges — Slugs
       with large tunnels — Wireworms (Fig. 20b)
       with small, black lesions — Symphylids

3. Seed tubers partly eaten — see *Damage to tubers* (page 9)

Damage to the growing crop

1. Patches of stunted growth, foliage yellowing or wilting (Fig. 1a):

    a. Roots with dark brown lesions — Needle nematodes
Root-lesion nematodes (Fig. 2a)
Symphylids (Fig. 2b)

    b. Proliferation of fine roots and later with cysts — white, yellow or brown — Potato cyst nematodes (Fig. 1b)

    c. With galls — Root-knot nematodes

    d. Without cysts or galls — Residual herbicide

Symptoms	Causes
2. Foliage distorted, with or without discoloration:	
a. Leaves rolled —	
lower leaves rolled and brittle	Potato leaf roll virus (secondary symptoms) (Fig. 3)
upper leaves rolled, sometimes reddened	Potato leaf roll virus (primary symptoms)
upper leaves rolled, aphids or cast skins present ('false top roll')	Aphids (Fig. 4)
upper leaves severely rolled, lower leaves blackened, plant with rosette-like appearance	Black leg (Fig. 5)
leaves curled, brown or blackened	Frost (Fig. 6)
b. Leaves stunted —	
leaves and stems stunted, twisted and swollen	Stem nematode (Fig. 13) Herbicide
leaves mottled, plant stunted (severe mosaic)	Potato virus Y
c. Leaves puckered — upper leaves puckered with pale or reddish spots often shredded and holed	Capsid bugs (Fig. 7)
3. Foliage discoloured but not distorted:	
a. Leaves with pale green or yellow mottling (mild mosaic)	Potato virus A Potato virus X Potato virus Y
b. Leaves with sharply defined whitish speckling	Leafhoppers
c. Leaves with discrete brown spots	Manganese deficiency
d. Leaves with marginal scorch	Nutrient deficiency Phytotoxicity
e. General yellowing of leaves	Aphids Nitrogen deficiency
f. Leaves yellow with necrotic lesions	Manganese toxicity
4. Foliage torn or partly eaten:	
a. Leaves shredded with pits on stalks and stems	Hailstones (Fig. 8)
b. Small, roundish 'shot-holes'	Potato flea beetle

Symptoms	Causes

   c. Upper leaves puckered, shredded and holed — Capsid bugs (Fig. 7)

   d. Irregular areas of leaf eaten, surface of stem grazed and slime present — Slugs (Fig. 9)

   e. Leaves eaten, mainly at margin, caterpillar and/or excrement present — Caterpillars (various) (Fig. 10)

   f. Severe defoliation, bright red larvae with black spots *or* black and yellow striped beetles present — Colorado beetle* (Plates 8b, 8c)

5. Stalks almost or completely severed at ground level — Cutworms (Fig. 11) / Leatherjackets

6. Shoots tunnelled and wilting, caterpillar present — Caterpillar of rosy rustic moth or frosted orange moth (Fig. 12)

7. Axillary buds swollen forming green, tuber-like structures (Fig. 14) — Damage to stem base, e.g. by machinery, weather or rhizoctonia

Damage to tubers

1. Tubers holed:

   a. Shallow, clean holes — Cutworms (Fig. 15a)

   b. Deep holes with tooth or beak marks — Rodents (Fig. 15b) / Birds

   c. Large cavities containing —

   an elongate white caterpillar — Caterpillar of swift moth (Fig.16a)

   a grey-white, curved, stout larva — Chafer grub (Fig. 16b)

   d. Shallow cavities with ragged edges, often associated with rotting tissue — Millipedes (Plate 7d)

   e. Fairly small entrance holes leading to larger internal cavities, slime often present — Slugs (Figs. 17a, 17b)

   f. Small, round entrance holes leading to narrow tunnels with blackened walls — Wireworms (Figs. 18a, 18b)

   g. Small round holes with clean edges and sides; tuber penetrated by hard, pointed rhizomes often pulled out during lifting — Couch-grass

*A potato pest not yet established in Britain, see page 92

Symptoms	Causes
2. Tubers with surface depressions:	
a. Small, circular pits, not corky and not penetrating skin	Ants (Plate 7c)
b. Similar pits with corky lining	Wireworms Larvae of bibionid flies
c. Large, discoloured depressions	Dry rot Gangrene Other fungus diseases
d. Shallow, depressed areas —	
skin cracked with dry, greyish-brown mealy tissue just below skin	Potato tuber nematode (Fig. 19a)
some skin cracking, greyish spongy tissue penetrating deep into tuber	Stem nematode
3. Tubers with surface swellings or blemishes:	
a. Smooth-skinned, round swellings	Physiological Varietal trait
b. Smooth-skinned, low swellings showing translucent spots below surface	Root-knot nematodes
c. Rough-skinned, low swellings —	
with white cysts emerging on to surface	Potato cyst nematodes (Plate 2a)
without cysts	Scab
4. Tubers showing internal damage when cut open:	
a. Areas of grey, blue or black discoloration	Potato tuber nematode (Fig. 19b) Stem nematode Blight Bruising
b. Rusty-brown internal markings	'Spraing' caused by tobacco rattle virus (Fig. 20a) Other viruses Frost
c. Star-shaped internal cavities ('hollow heart')	Tuber re-growth after drought

Further reading

ADAS Identification Cards 151–170. *Potato diseases and disorders*. Ministry of Agriculture, Fisheries and Food, London.

ANON. (1981). *Diagnosis of Herbicide Damage to Crops*. Reference Book of the Ministry of Agriculture, Fisheries and Food, London, No. 221. HMSO.

ANON. (1985). *Plant Physiological Disorders*. Reference Book of the Ministry of Agriculture, Fisheries and Food, London, No. 223. HMSO.

BRENCHLEY, G. H. and WILCOX, H. J. (1979). *Potato Diseases*. RPD1 of the Ministry of Agriculture, Fisheries and Food, London. HMSO.

HOOKER, W. J. (Ed.) (1981). *Compendium of Potato Diseases*. St. Paul, Minnesota, USA: The American Phytopathological Society.

RICH, AVERY, E. (1983). *Potato Diseases*. London: Academic Press.

WALLACE, T. (1943 and Supplement 1944). *The Diagnosis of Mineral Deficiencies in Plants by Visual Symptoms. A Colour Atlas and Guide*. London: HMSO.

Fig. 1a. Potato cyst nematode damage symptoms — affected and healthy plants

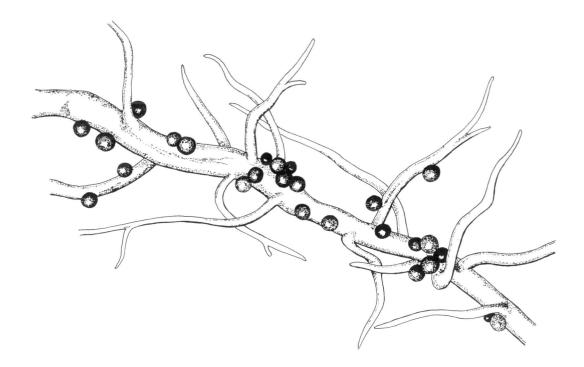

Fig. 1b. Potato cyst nematode cysts on roots

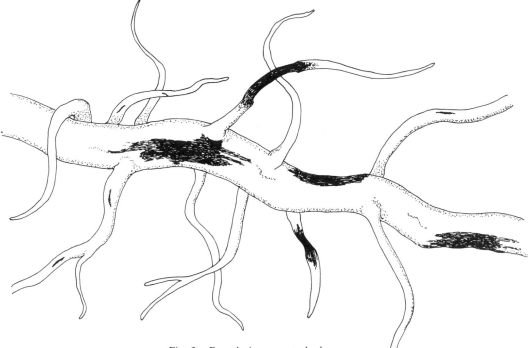

Fig. 2a. Root-lesion nematode damage

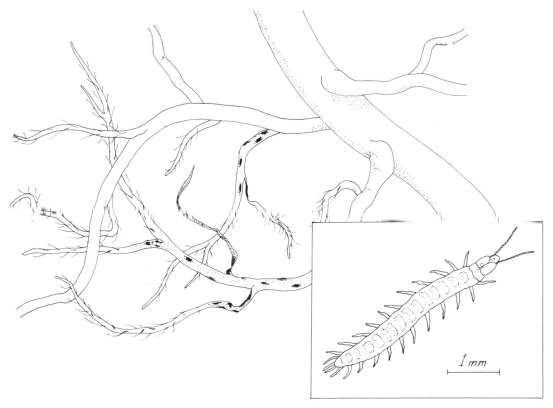

Fig. 2b. Symphylid damage to roots with symphylid inset

Fig. 3. Leaf roll (caused by potato leaf roll virus)

Fig. 4. False top roll (caused by aphids)

Fig. 5. Black leg (caused by a pathogen)

Fig. 6. Severe frost damage to foliage

Fig. 7. Capsid damage to foliage

Fig. 8. Hail damage to foliage and stem

Fig. 9. Slug damage to foliage and stem

Fig. 10. Caterpillar damage to foliage

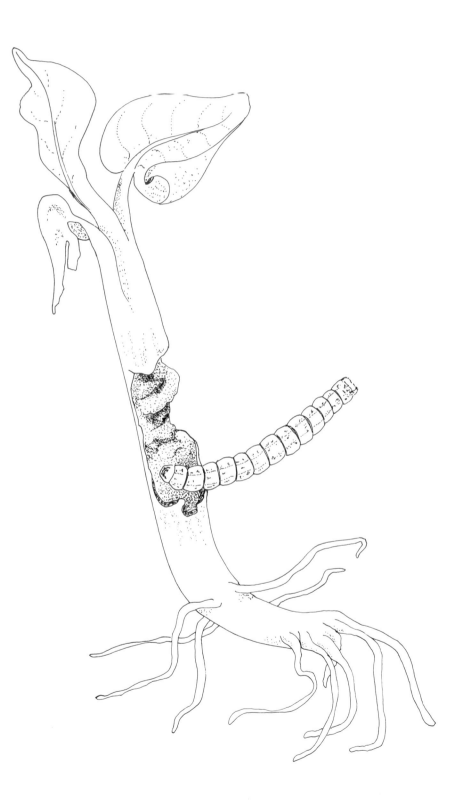

Fig. 11. Cutworm damage to stem

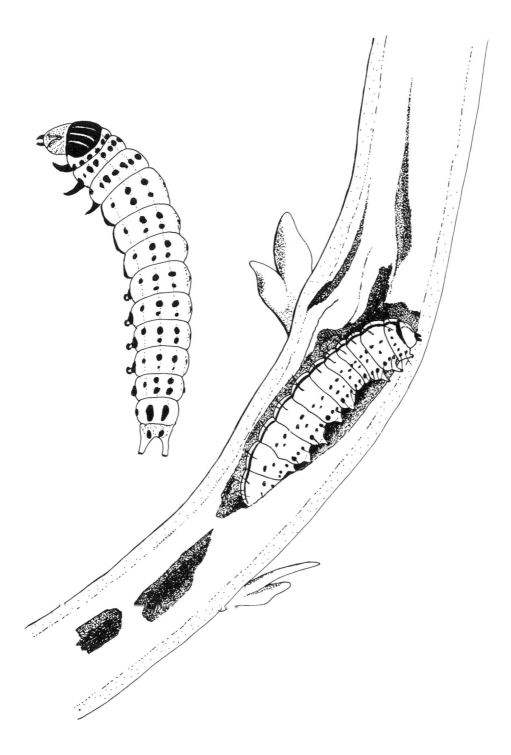

Fig. 12. Rosy rustic moth caterpillar (about twice natural size) in damaged stem with frosted orange moth caterpillar, which causes similar damage, alongside

Fig. 13. Stem nematode damage to foliage and stem

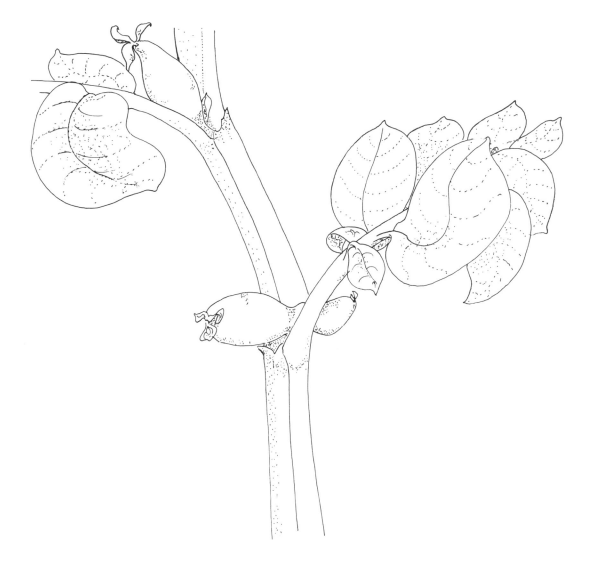

Fig. 14. Malformation of axillary buds following damage to stem base

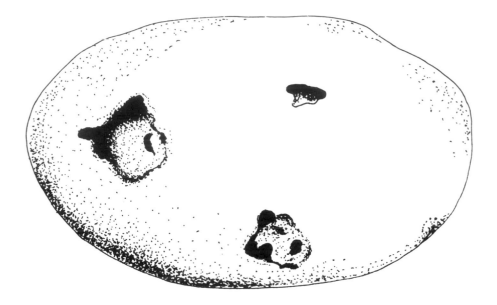

Fig. 15a. Cutworm damage to tuber

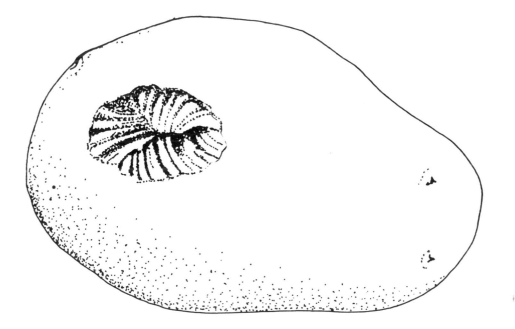

Fig. 15b. Rodent damage to tuber

26

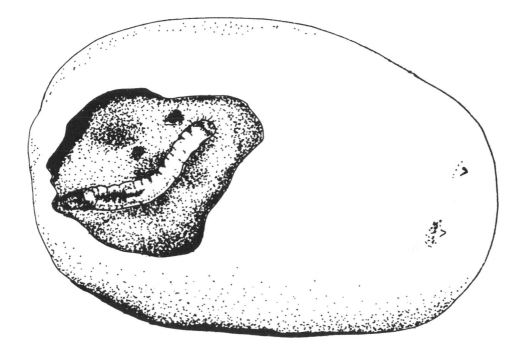

Fig. 16a. Swift moth caterpillar damage to tuber with caterpillar in position

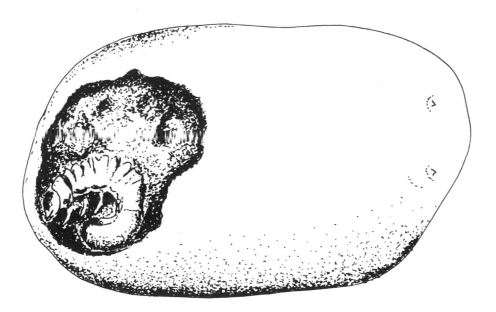

Fig. 16b. Chafer grub damage to tuber with grub in position

27

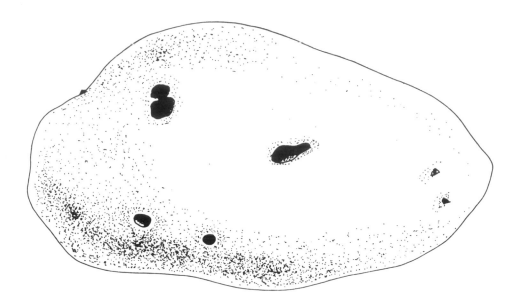

Fig. 17a. Slug damage to tuber — external view

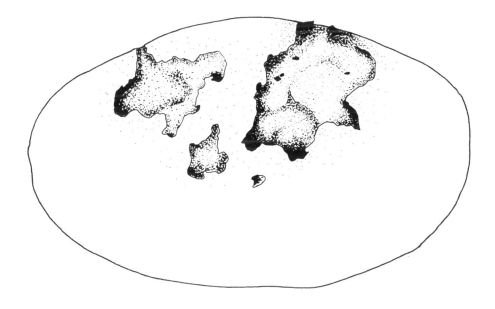

Fig. 17b. Slug damage to tuber — cut open to show internal view

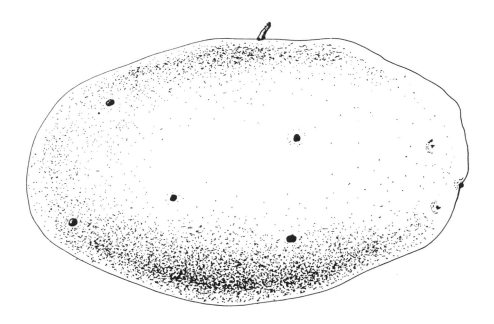

Fig. 18a. Wireworm damage to tuber — external view

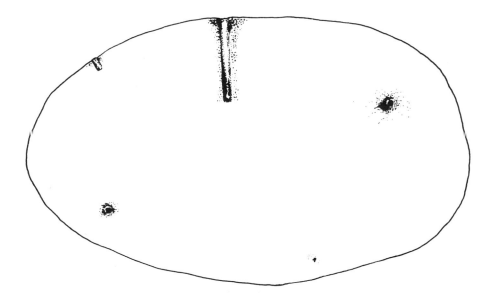

Fig. 18b. Wireworm damage to tuber — cut open to show internal view

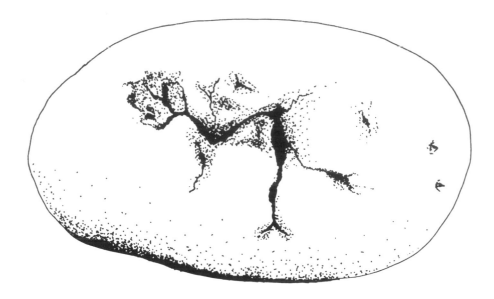

Fig. 19a. Potato tuber nematode damage — external view of tuber

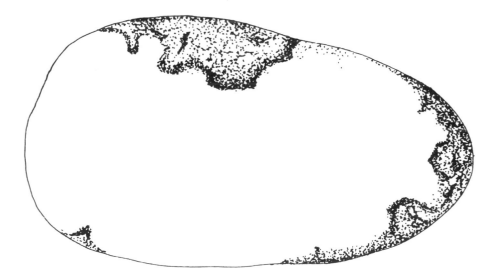

Fig. 19b. Potato tuber nematode damage — tuber cut open to show internal view

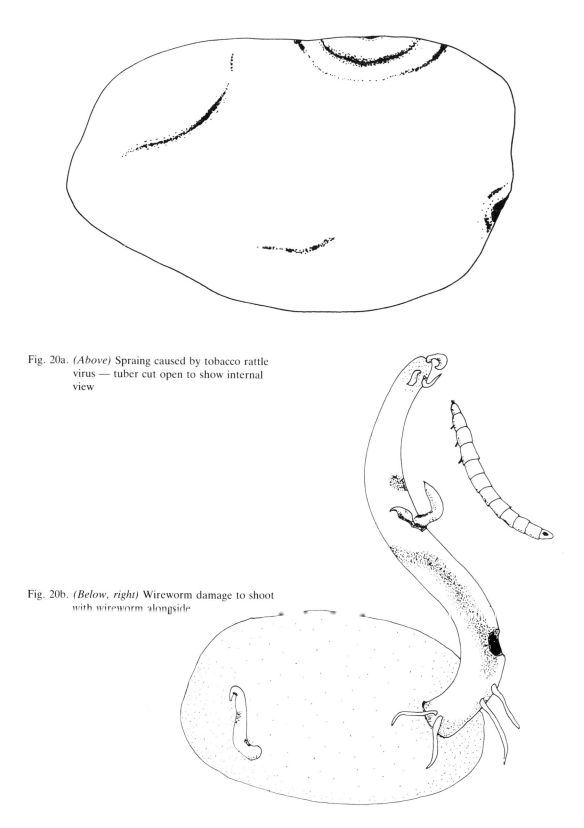

Fig. 20a. *(Above)* Spraing caused by tobacco rattle virus — tuber cut open to show internal view

Fig. 20b. *(Below, right)* Wireworm damage to shoot with wireworm alongside

Prevention and control of pest damage

Prevention of damage

Losses due to pest attack can be considerable. It has been estimated that, if no steps at all were taken to avoid pest damage, one-ninth of the potential potato crop in England and Wales would be lost. Modern crop protection programmes exploit the advantages of crop rotation and resistant varieties, thereby lessening the need for pesticides. Nevertheless the use of pesticides is substantial. The mean number of all insecticide, nematicide and molluscicide treatments applied to each hectare of a potato crop was 1.2 in 1982. Of the area treated, about 70 per cent received aphicidal sprays, 28 per cent granules that were aphicidal and/or nematicidal and about one per cent molluscicides. The large aphid populations which built up during 1974–76 led to greatly increased use of aphicides on both ware and seed potato crops. Probably the most marked change during the past 10 years has been an increase in the use of chemicals which are primarily nematicidal, especially in areas where the presence of the white potato cyst nematode precludes the use of resistant varieties (see page 42).

The total expenditure on insecticides, nematicides and molluscicides used on the potato crop in England, Scotland and Wales in 1984 has been estimated as £3.8 million. An unknown proportion of this expenditure would have been unnecessary or ineffective. However, as crop yield potential and inputs increase, a comprehensive crop protection programme to prevent low levels of pest damage may be necessary to safeguard the investment by ensuring the high quality of tubers required by the market. The benefits of pesticide usage are difficult to quantify accurately on a national basis. However, as an example of the value of combining soil sampling to predict the presence of potato cyst nematodes with the use of resistant varieties and nematicides, the benefit to the 14 000 hectares of potatoes grown in the Isle of Ely (about 10 per cent of the national area) was judged to be about £2.6 million in 1980. Extending this to the whole of England and Wales, but with less emphasis on nematode control since the Isle of Ely is more affected by potato cyst nematodes than many other areas, a total of £18 million was indicated as accruing from effective pest control. At £50 per tonne the total cost represented some 360 000 tonnes of marketable potatoes – a figure not very different from the initial estimate of 11 per cent of the national crop. It also indicates a 6 : 1 return on the investment in chemical control.

For seed producers, classification of their crops is crucial to success, so greater use of aphicides can be justified than on the ware crop and is in fact common, especially where aphids are more of a problem – that is outside the climatically favourable areas for seed growing.

To keep matters in perspective however, the potential loss from potato blight in an epidemic year and in the absence of chemical control would be substantially greater than the total losses from all pest damage.

Thus, control by chemical methods is expensive. The best and, in the long run, the most efficient way of preventing losses due to pests is to alter the conditions of growth so that the balance of advantage is in favour of the crop and against the pest.

The major contribution to pest and disease damage is overcropping; rotation is therefore of great importance. If potatoes are grown continuously in the same ground, there can be a build-up of organisms which attack the crop and a deterioration in the soil structure. Poorer soil conditions lead to poorer growth and to an increasing susceptibility to attack by pests or diseases. The acceptable length of rotation depends on the condition of the soil and on the extent to which pest populations have already increased. A four-year rotation is probably safe under most circumstances in the absence of potato cyst nematodes. Where potato cyst nematodes are present, it may be possible to use pesticides and/or resistant varieties to restrict them to a level at which normal rotation can be continued, whereas in the past an initial long rest would have been necessary.

The beneficial effects of rotation may be lost if pests are allowed to enter the crop from outside. There is, of course, no effective way of preventing arrivals of airborne aphids or of nematodes in 'soil blows', but some pests arrive either with the seed tubers or in soil. The use of classified seed can reduce the danger of tuber-borne attacks. Most native or long-established soil-borne pests of potato, including potato cyst nematodes, are already widely distributed in the many potato-producing areas. Therefore, elaborate precautions to prevent spread are pointless. However, it is sensible to avoid unnecessary transport of soil likely to be infested.

Just as rotation and hygiene can shift the balance against the pest, so proper cultivation can adjust it in favour of the crop. Correct cultivation, drainage and manuring can all contribute to the production of a crop which can withstand low levels of pest attack. One aspect of good cultivation that can easily be overlooked is timely lifting. As soon as the foliage ceases to be green (through natural senescence, blight or burning-off), it makes no further contribution to the crop and little is lost by lifting the tubers. If the tubers are left in the ground after they have ripened, the proportion damaged by slugs, wireworms and other tuber-feeding pests can start to rise steeply.

Plants living in a balanced wild community have evolved their own means of combating natural enemies; human selection for greater yield and palatability has led to the loss of many of these mechanisms in cultivated crop plants. But the potential is still present in the wild ancestors of many food crops, so that plant breeders in the last few decades have not only selected for pest and disease resistance among cultivated varieties but have gone back to the wild ancestors and isolated the genetic factors responsible for their resistance. These genes are gradually being introduced into new varieties, which combine resistance with acceptable commercial properties. There are still problems to be overcome, for selection within the pest population sometimes reveals 'resistance-breaking' types and necessitates a further breeding programme. Nevertheless, resistant varieties are already making a great contribution to the control of pests, especially potato cyst nematodes, and more resistant varieties are being developed.

Principles and methods of control

The best method of controlling any individual pest depends on a knowledge of the biology of both pest and host plant; methods for particular pests are described in the following chapters and only general principles are outlined here.

Pesticides

Pesticides may be classified in several ways. One way is by the type of organism on which they act: thus insects are killed by insecticides, nematodes by nematicides, mites by acaricides, slugs and snails by molluscicides, rats and mice by rodenticides, etc. The general term pesticide is now often used to include fungicides, which control diseases, and even herbicides, which kill weeds.

Another method of classification is by the mode of action. A *'stomach poison'* must be eaten before it is effective; it will act on animals which bite into the tissues but does little or no harm to species which settle on the plant or suck its sap. A *'contact poison'*, by contrast, acts through the cuticle or skin of the animal; there is no need for plant tissues to be eaten and there is, consequently, considerable risk of harm to beneficial species. Some of the most efficient contact poisons are also very persistent and may, like many of the organochlorine pesticides, have unwanted side-effects far from the intended site of action. It is possible to produce contact poisons which affect only a small range of organisms, but such selective chemicals are likely to be more costly, as well as creating marketing difficulties. A *'fumigant'* acts as a vapour and can therefore reach pests which are protected by foliage or soil, but unless it is confined it will quickly diffuse; thus it has little persistence and leaves little residue. A *'systemic chemical'* is one which is absorbed by a plant and translocated within the tissues so that the whole plant becomes poisonous to the pest; this is the ideal method for controlling sap-sucking pests, but by its nature can create a problem with toxic residues unless broken down or eliminated from the plant within a reasonable time.

Classification may also be on the basis of the physical form of the pesticide – dust, granule, wettable powder, emulsifiable concentrate, etc. The choice of the correct formulation may have a marked effect on the success of control measures. The method of application may determine the acceptability or otherwise of a particular control method. Sprays or dusts applied from the air, and dusts or fumigants incorporated in the soil, make relatively inefficient use of large quantities of material; their use may have highly undesirable consequences for the environment. At the other extreme, seed treatments, dips, or granular materials applied with a precision applicator, make more efficient use of much smaller quantities of material; the pesticide is applied only at the point where it is needed, so that the total amount reaching the environment is much smaller and highly poisonous chemicals may be used without danger to the environment, the user or the ultimate consumer.

Pesticides may also be classified according to their chemical structure. Most of those available for commercial use on potato fall into four main groups: carbamates, organochlorines, organophosphorus compounds and synthetic pyrethroids.
Carbamate compounds: carbofuran, methiocarb and pirimicarb. Closely related to the carbamates and usually grouped with them are aldicarb, oxamyl and thiofanox. All those quoted are insecticides although methiocarb is used primarily as a molluscicide. Aldicarb, carbofuran and oxamyl are also nematicides. Carbamate and carbamate-type compounds are mainly available in granular form.

Organochlorine compounds: aldrin, dichloropropene and gamma-HCH. Aldrin now has very restricted use on potato and is to be phased out in the early 1990s. Dichloropropene is a liquid nematicide used as a soil fumigant. Gamma-HCH smoke is approved for use as an aphicide in potato stores.

Organophosphorus compounds: chlorpyrifos, demeton-S-methyl, dimethoate, disulfoton, heptenophos, malathion, oxydemeton-methyl, phorate, thiometon, triazophos and trichlorphon. These are all insecticides. They are mainly acute poisons, but because of their relatively short persistence they do not appear to affect wildlife populations. All except malathion, chlorpyrifos, triazophos and trichlorphon act systemically. Most of them are available only as sprays but two, disulfoton and phorate, are in granular form, which increases their persistence; trichlorphon is formulated as a soluble powder. Organophosphorus insecticides have been widely used on potato primarily for aphid control. The development of peach–potato aphids that are resistant to several of these chemicals is a problem which became apparent in the late 1970s (see page 74). Highly resistant aphids have been found in many parts of Britain including eastern England, the Midlands, southern Scotland and especially northern England. This will inevitably mean a restriction in the range of insecticides giving effective control. Chlorpyrifos, triazophos and trichlorphon are not used as aphicides on potato but control some other insect pests.

Pyrethroid compounds: alphacypermethrin, cypermethrin and deltamethrin. These are all insecticides available as sprays. On potato, alphacypermethrin and cypermethrin are used to control caterpillars. A product containing a mixture of deltamethrin and the organophosphorus compound heptenophos is used as an aphicide.

Others: copper sulphate, dazomet, metham-sodium, metaldehyde and nicotine. These compounds do not belong to any of the four main groups already described. Dazomet and metham-sodium are soil sterilants used against nematodes, soil-borne diseases and weeds. Metaldehyde is a polymer of acetaldehyde and is a molluscicide. Copper sulphate is also used as a molluscicide. Nicotine is an insecticide recommended for aphid control in potato chitting houses.

Integrated control

The term 'integrated control' is used when various types of control method are combined in a unified programme so that they complement one another's action and a method used against one pest does not conflict with that needed for another. The section on potato cyst nematodes (see pages 45–7) describes an example of the integration of rotation, nematicides and resistant varieties.

Regulatory control

Measures for prevention and control of serious pests and diseases are made compulsory by government regulations when it is judged that voluntary action is insufficient to ensure the degree of control required in the national or in the European Community interest. Plant health regulations fall under two main headings: *import legislation* intended primarily to prevent the introduction from abroad of non-indigenous pests and diseases, but also to safeguard the general standard of health of imported planting material (including seed potatoes); and *domestic legislation* to restrict the spread and/or build-up of certain economically serious pests, particularly those whose distribution had not reached its full potential when legislation was introduced.

Regulations concerning potato cyst nematodes are discussed on page 47 and those for Colorado beetle are referred to on page 93. The Seed Potato Regulations 1978 provide graded sources of seed potatoes of specified minimum standards of health and purity (see page 68).

Further reading

ANON. (1961). *Seed Potatoes. The Maintenance of Pure, Healthy and Vigorous Stocks*. Department of Agriculture and Fisheries for Scotland. Edinburgh: HMSO.

DAVIDSON, W. D. (1937). *Potato Growing for Seed Purposes*. Dublin: The Stationery Office.

SLY, J. M. A. (1986). Arable farm crops and grass 1982. *Pesticide Usage Survey Report* 35. Reference Book of the Ministry of Agriculture, Fisheries and Food, London, No. 535. MAFF.

Nematodes

Nematodes are slender (eel-shaped), unsegmented, round worms. They are a large and diverse group of invertebrates which live in soil, in fresh or marine water, or are parasitic on or within plant or animal tissues.

With a few exceptions, such as the cyst stage of potato cyst nematodes, the species attacking plants are too small to be seen easily without magnification: most are between 0.5 and 1.5 mm in length when fully grown. The majority of plant-feeding nematodes live in association with the roots or other underground structures such as bulbs, corms and tubers, though stems and leaves can also be infested. A piercing mouth-spear or stylet is used to penetrate plant tissue when feeding; some species transmit virus diseases during this process. Those nematodes which live exclusively in the soil and feed externally on roots, tubers etc. are termed ectoparasites, e.g. stubby-root nematodes. Others, which spend most of their life cycle within plant tissue, are endoparasites; these may be relatively immobile or sedentary, e.g. potato cyst nematodes, or mobile within the plant, e.g. stem nematode. All these types are represented among the nematode pests of potato (Table 1).

Table 1. Nematodes attacking potatoes

Type of attack	Common name	Scientific name
Below ground on roots		
(a) endoparasitic – sedentary	potato cyst nematodes	*Globodera* spp.
	root-knot nematodes*	*Meloidogyne* spp.
	false root-knot nematodes*	*Nacobbus* spp.
(b) endoparasitic – mobile	root-lesion nematodes	*Pratylenchus* spp.
(c) ectoparasitic – mobile	needle nematodes	*Longidorus* spp.
	stubby-root nematodes+	*Trichodorus* spp. *Paratrichodorus* spp.
Below ground on tubers		
(d) endoparasitic – mobile	potato tuber nematode	*Ditylenchus destructor*
	stem nematode	*Ditylenchus dipsaci*
On stems and leaves		
(e) endoparasitic – mobile	stem nematode	*Ditylenchus dipsaci*

*Not found on potatoes in UK
+Virus vectors

POTATO CYST NEMATODES

Distribution and spread

The potato cyst nematodes (*Globodera* spp.) are well established and serious pests in most parts of the world where the potato crop has been grown intensively (Fig. 21). Until 1973 the pest was thought to comprise a single species, *Heterodera rostochiensis*, although different strains or pathotypes were recognised.

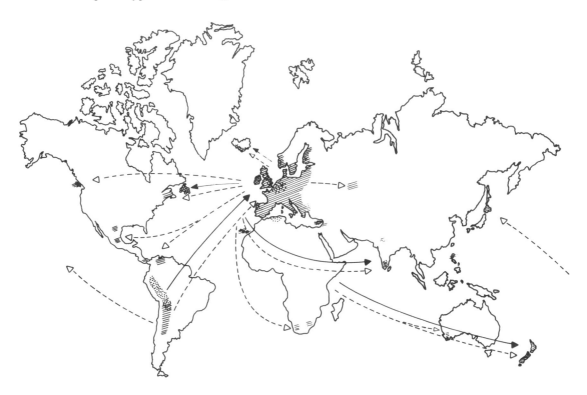

Fig. 21. World dispersal of the two species of potato cyst nematode from their centres of origin in the Andes. (Based on Jones and Kempton, in Southey, 1978). (Diagonal lines — *Globodera rostochiensis*; stippling — *G. pallida*)

In 1881 Kühn reported a cyst-forming nematode attacking potatoes in Germany. By 1913 the pest was recognised as common in Scotland; in about 1916 its presence was confirmed in Yorkshire and subsequent enquiries pointed to its presence in the Hull area from about 1900. By the early 1920s, potato sickness associated with cyst nematode was being widely reported in most of the traditional ware-potato areas of Britain. It is thought to have been introduced during the mid-1800s when there was an intensive search for blight-resistant varieties and when much potato breeding material was imported from South America.

Cysts can be carried on seed tubers and in soil and are moved from place to place by wind, flood water, farm machinery and implements as well as with plants (other than potato) grown for transplanting. There is little chance, therefore, that the pest has not been introduced to all the major areas of ware-potato production.

Ware-potato growing in England and Wales is concentrated in four major areas, namely (i) South Yorkshire and north Lincolnshire, (ii) south Lincolnshire and the Fens, (iii) west Lancashire and (iv) the West Midlands, with smaller areas scattered round the larger conurbations. The areas of greatest nematode density coincide with those of greatest potato density and hence the location of the greatest crop losses until more effective control measures became available in the 1970s. However, in south-west England, Pembrokeshire, Kent, south Essex and Suffolk there are early-potato areas where the nematode is frequently found, but where it seldom causes economic crop losses. Here the crops are lifted before many of the nematodes have had time to complete a new generation.

Potato cyst nematodes are subject to stringent plant quarantine regulations in many countries, and the importation of plants, nursery stock and particularly potato tubers is strictly controlled. Plant health certification schemes, closely controlled seed-potato production and plant quarantine regulations help to delay the introduction, minimise spread and lessen the effects of the pest. These measures are particularly important for geographically isolated areas known or believed to be free from potato cyst nematodes. However, in areas already known or likely to be infested, such regulations contribute little to the control of the pest. Here the emphasis should be on educational and advisory programmes, farm hygiene, careful crop-recording and the sensible integration of rotational and chemical control measures with the use of resistant varieties.

Description and life history

The potato cyst nematodes belong to the group of cyst nematodes that have round cysts (genus *Globodera*). This is distinct from the group that has lemon-shaped cysts (*Heterodera*) and the grass cyst nematode (*Punctodera punctata*), which has oval cysts.

The cyst is the dead female nematode and may contain up to 600 eggs. Cysts are usually about 0.5 mm in diameter and hence just visible to the unaided eye. Each egg has a young nematode (juvenile) curled inside it; one moult occurs in the egg so that on hatching the juveniles are in their second stage. In the spring up to one third of the eggs may hatch spontaneously, i.e. in the absence of a host plant, and the young nematodes escape from the cyst into the soil (Plate 1b). Unless these juveniles find a suitable host they eventually die, although they can live free in the soil for several weeks. In Britain the only cultivated host plants are potato, tomato and aubergine. Other members of the family Solanaceae, for example bittersweet (*Solanum dulcamara* L.) and black nightshade (*S. nigrum* L.) are poor hosts. It is rare to find cysts on roots of weed hosts in Britain.

The rate of spontaneous hatching is influenced by climate, field aspect and soil type; large variations also occur from year to year and even within fields in the same season. The factors governing hatching have been the subject of much research during the last 40 years. The second-stage juveniles within the cyst remain at low metabolic activity until stimulated or triggered to hatch by specific stimuli, including the presence of a range of chemical substances. When potatoes are grown in infested soil, root diffusates from the crop stimulate a massive hatch of eggs during April and May, sometimes continuing into the summer; many of these newly hatched juveniles invade the potato roots. However, as many as one third of the eggs fail to hatch in the presence of the host crop. This is a valuable survival mechanism, although some of these eggs will hatch the following year when no host plants are present and the young nematodes will perish. Thus, in the absence of host crops, nematode populations decline gradually. Rotational control depends on this decline but many years elapse before all the eggs hatch. The rate of decline is generally in the range 10–30 per cent annually but depends on many factors including soil type; it tends to be slower on organic soils than on mineral soils.

When the juveniles find the root of a host plant they invade it, sometimes by piercing the epidermal cells with their stylets, but most often through cracks and crevices where the lateral rootlets emerge from the main root. They embed themselves in the cortex near the conducting tissue of the root, which responds by forming a multinucleate food-transfer cell, known as a *syncytium*, in which the head of the nematode remains embedded until maturity. Failure to form a transfer cell almost invariably results in the death of the nematode.

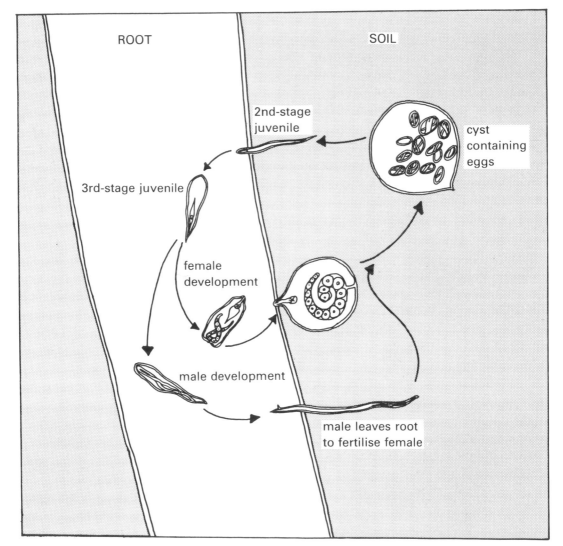

Fig. 22. Life cycle of potato cyst nematodes

The sex ratio of the juveniles is controlled genetically and to some extent by the density of nematodes inside the host root. When the juveniles are severely overcrowded the food-transfer cells are smaller, which leads to a greater proportion of males. When there is no overcrowding a larger proportion become females.

As a response to invasion, the plant produces many lateral roots, especially near the soil surface, and fresh laterals produced early in the season may also be invaded. The nematodes grow and swell, first becoming flask-shaped. After the final moult within the root, the males, which have become worm-like, force their way out into the soil moisture film. The females meanwhile swell and burst out of the root, remaining attached to it by the head. The females emit powerful chemical substances that attract the males so that mating can occur; each female can be mated several times. During June, July and early August the newly formed females may be seen with the unaided eye as tiny bead-like bodies along the roots. Usually they are most abundant on roots larger than 0.5 mm in diameter, although some may be seen on thinner roots; it is important to lift plants for inspection very carefully as roots and female nematodes are easily broken off. Towards the end of August and through potato lifting-time until the following spring, cysts fall off the roots into the soil. Some cysts may adhere to pieces of dead root tissue for several years. When the soil is very heavily infested, large numbers of newly formed females may be seen on tubers (Plate 2a) and stolons as well as on roots. Some of the tuber-borne females are embedded, usually in or near the 'eyes', and this is probably one of the means by which the pest is spread.

When females first appear on the roots they are glistening white; later they pass through a series of colour changes until they become fully tanned and dark brown — they may then be termed cysts. The immature females of the yellow potato cyst nematode, *Globodera rostochiensis*, have a conspicuous golden-yellow phase (Plate 1a, left), lasting between three and six weeks during July/August. Females of the white potato cyst nematode, *G. pallida*, have a prolonged white or creamy-white phase (Plate 1a, right) and a very short lemon-yellow phase before the cyst tans a deeper brown.

Resistant potato varieties

During the last 30 years or so potato varieties have been bred by crossing South American tuber-forming *Solanums*, especially *Solanum tuberosum* sub-species *andigena* (Juz. et Buk.) Hawkes, with the commonly cultivated potato *S. tuberosum*. This plant breeding work revealed differences in the ability of nematode populations to multiply on different potato hybrids even though invasion always occurs. These differences in virulence are now known to exist both between and within the two species of nematode. Strains differing in virulence are known as pathotypes. The *andigena* hybrids possess the H1 gene that confers complete resistance to pathotypes Ro1 and Ro4 of *G. rostochiensis*. At present, no resistance-breaking pathotypes of *G. rostochiensis* are known in this country, but in the Netherlands, West Germany and possibly other parts of mainland Europe some pathotypes (Ro2, Ro3 and Ro5) are able to breed on potato varieties with H1 resistance. In Britain the known pathotypes of *G. pallida* (Pa1 and Pa2/3) multiply on potatoes with H1 resistance only. Some of the *Solanum* species used in plant breeding programmes have polygenic resistance which confers on their hybrids a partial or quantitative resistance to both species. In those areas with a predominance of *G. rostochiensis*, varieties with the H1 gene will have maximum effect in reducing the nematode population; as the proportion of *G. pallida* increases, these varieties will become less useful.

Fig. 23 shows the approximate known distribution of *G. pallida* and *G. rostochiensis* in the principal areas of England where maincrop potatoes are grown. With experience a farmer may be able to use cyst coloration as an aid to determining the species distribution on his farm. Cyst coloration is particularly useful for detecting *G. pallida* on varieties with the H1 gene. However, laboratory identification is necessary for accurate determination of the species of nematode present.

Varieties resistant to *G. rostochiensis* are cited in the National Institute of Agricultural Botany's recommended list. At present there are no varieties fully resistant to *G. pallida*, but some partially resistant varieties are available.

Fig. 23. Known occurrence of the two species of potato cyst nematode in the principal areas of England growing maincrop potatoes. (Based on Jones, 1970).

42

No potato variety is immune from attack. Resistant varieties are invaded but the nematodes fail to mature and die. At high initial nematode densities the damage caused by invading juveniles, even to resistant varieties, may be so severe that the plants do not recover. Even on a field with a moderate initial nematode density, an economic crop cannot be guaranteed from a resistant variety unless a nematicide is also used (see page 44).

Population changes

The initial introduction of the pest to fields is most likely to be a random scattering of cysts or clumps of cysts. Lateral spread of infestation from a single viable cyst is probably less than 1/10 metre each year. Build-up of populations to damaging levels is directly attributable to frequent cropping. When potatoes are grown in a close rotation nematode numbers build up very rapidly and damaging levels are reached within a comparatively short time. In practice, potato crops are seldom grown continuously, so that nematode levels decline between crops and the time taken to reach severe levels is usually extended. The length of time that elapses between first detection and 'potato sickness' depends on the frequency of cropping and the interaction between the nematodes, fungus diseases and adverse soil conditions.

Population increase is greatest when initial density is lowest, and least when nematodes are numerous before cropping. As densities increase, competition for feeding sites in the roots limits population increase. Thus, at high initial densities final populations may be no greater than they were before cropping. The population changes that may occur during a single growing season depend on the proportion of the initial (pre-cropping) population that remains unhatched, the number of new cysts produced and the number of eggs in each new cyst. When nematodes hatch but do not breed, final numbers will be less than those present at the start of the season. Factors causing such a decline include a year's rest from potatoes (up to 33 per cent decrease) and growing a variety resistant to the pathotype present (about 67 per cent decrease). The use of a fumigant nematicide can decrease the pre-planting population by up to 95 per cent. It is possible, using a combination of rotation, resistant varieties and a nematicide, i.e. integrated control, to produce an even greater decrease in the nematode population (see pages 45–7). The amount of damage caused to roots by the invading nematodes affects their survival and multiplication so that when roots are small, badly damaged, or when initial numbers are large, a larger proportion fail to survive and the multiplication rate is lower. Also, much depends on the vigour of the crop, the weather and soil conditions during the growing season and the ability of the variety to yield well despite nematode attack, i.e. tolerance. The more tolerant a susceptible variety is the greater the multiplication rate will be.

When growing susceptible varieties a rotation of one in eight years should ensure that nematode numbers do not rise to unacceptable levels. A closer rotation, such as one in five years, will in most circumstances not allow an adequate decline in the population between potato crops to prevent subsequent economic losses. A very close rotation, e.g. one in three, invariably allows nematode numbers to increase to damaging levels. Other potato disorders are almost certain to increase in a close rotation and these will add to the losses suffered from nematode damage.

In some instances volunteer plants (also known as groundkeepers or self-sets) may reduce the rate of decline of the population. It is therefore sound practice to destroy volunteers. The volunteer problem is especially serious with the nematode-resistant variety Maris Piper, which produces vigorous plants from very small chats. If volunteers grow unchecked for several successive seasons, resistance-breaking populations of nematodes may soon build up to serious levels.

Damage

Potato cyst nematodes reduce potato yield and this loss may or may not be accompanied by obvious symptoms in the haulm. Typically the damage appears as patches of stunted yellowing plants (Plate 1c). Failures occasionally occur at low nematode densities, perhaps due to an interaction with some disease or adverse soil condition. On some fertile soils large yields may be obtained even when nematode densities are high, so that yield losses pass unnoticed. The presence of cysts on the roots of stunted plants in patches does not necessarily mean that nematodes are the only problem: rhizoctonia and other diseases are often contributory causes of poor growth.

A crop can compensate for slight damage, but the degree of compensation depends on the time of damage in relation to crop maturity. As pest numbers increase, a threshold point is reached beyond which damage increases rapidly for each additional increment in pest numbers and for which the crop is unable to compensate. In a large number of field experiments in the eastern and midland counties of England over the last 25 years, it was shown that yield losses could often be predicted fairly accurately from pre-cropping nematode counts, being of similar magnitude on high- and low-yielding crops. However, it has been suggested recently that there is considerable and significant variation between sites in the damage caused by potato cyst nematodes and that yield response to oximecarbamate nematicides in the presence of nematodes cannot be accurately predicted; yields are not, however, increased at most uninfested sites. Several factors almost certainly interact either to increase or decrease nematode damage: for example, differences in yield potential between sites, differences between varieties in their tolerance of damage, interactions with micro-organisms, and differences in husbandry.

Chemical control

There are now several oximecarbamate pesticides available for the control of potato cyst nematodes: aldicarb, carbofuran and oxamyl. All are formulated as granules. They are broadcast immediately before planting and then evenly worked into the top 10–15 cm of soil (field populations of potato cyst nematode are usually restricted to cultivation depth). The active ingredients are soluble in soil water and act by disrupting the nematodes' metabolism, feeding and movement but do not always kill them, i.e. nematostasis. These nematostatic compounds effectively control juveniles in the soil and can result in large crop responses.

In contrast to these nematostatic granules, the soil fumigants (dazomet, dichloropropene and metham-sodium) are nematicidal in action, killing nematodes in the soil and in the cysts. For greatest effect, these fumigants should be applied in the autumn at any stage in the rotation. Dazomet is formulated as a prill (fine granule) which is broadcast and incorporated in about the top 20 cm of soil. Dichloropropene and metham-sodium are liquids which are injected with specialised equipment to the same depth as dazomet. After application the surface of the soil must be sealed, usually by rolling or smearing, to prevent the gaseous nematicidal phase from escaping from the soil before it has had time to act. On certain soil types, such as heavy clays and peats, which are difficult to seal, fumigants are impracticable. Soil fumigants are phytotoxic so that it is important to ensure that there are no residues left in the soil at planting time.

The manufacturer's recommendations for application of granules and fumigants should be followed closely.

Although granules or fumigants generally give good yield responses, nematode densities after cropping are invariably greater than before, particularly with the fumigants. This is an important consideration when growing potatoes in close rotation.

Integrated control

The basis of potato cyst nematode control is sound crop rotation with the appropriate use of resistant varieties and chemicals, aided by soil sampling to determine population densities and species of nematode. Such an approach which combines two or more control measures is known as integrated control. The term 'integrated control', or 'integrated pest management', usually includes the use of natural enemies. So far, however, there is no evidence that there is any effective parasite or predator of potato cyst nematodes in Europe.

The effectiveness of integrated control is illustrated by two long-term experiments started in 1972 in eastern England. At Terrington Experimental Husbandry Farm (EHF) the effect of three control measures on an infestation of *G. rostochiensis* Ro1 was studied: (i) rotation — potatoes every three or six years; (ii) nematicide — aldicarb or oxamyl compared with no chemical; and (iii) variety — Maris Piper (a variety with Ro1 resistance) or King Edward (a standard susceptible variety) or an alternation of the two in the rotation. Nematicide treatment or the use of a resistant variety was highly successful in reducing numbers of potato cyst nematode and producing large yield increases. By 1983, even where nematode populations had been dramatically reduced over the years, there was still a yield benefit from using a nematicide and/or the longer of the two rotations.

At Arthur Rickwood EHF, a similar experiment included four- and six-year rotations instead of three and six years. As at Terrington, a very severe infestation of *G. rostochiensis* Ro1 was greatly reduced after two rotations in which an Ro1-resistant variety was grown with a pre-cropping application of a nematicide, this result was obtained for both the four- and six-year rotations.

Integrated control is successful because the combined measures reduce the nematode population to such an extent that the breeding capability of the nematode cannot compensate for the effect of the treatments. In fact, the combined effect of all three treatments can closely approach 100 per cent control. Rotation can give up to 30 per cent control for each year's rest from potatoes and a resistant variety up to 80 per cent control. A nematicide can result in up to 70–98 per cent control. The combined effect of these population reductions would have to be matched by a balancing multiplication if the pest were not to lose ground. When the control is less than 95 per cent the remaining population can easily achieve the balancing 20-fold multiplication required and thus restore the population level, so that after harvest it is equal to that existing before planting. However, an integrated control programme with a combined control of 99 per cent requires a balancing multiplication rate of 100-fold, usually but not always beyond the capacity of the nematode. Experiments have shown that the integration of rotation, resistant varieties and nematicides can successfully keep potato cyst nematodes under control.

The commercial use of integrated control against potato cyst nematodes has usually maintained the *status quo*, so that potato yields have increased and nematode populations have either remained static or increased only very slowly. However, the integrated control programme actually used is often a compromise between the need to control the pest and the need to keep the enterprise solvent. The rotation followed may well be shorter than ideal and nematode populations that are larger than desirable may have to be tolerated.

Sometimes the effective rotation is shortened inadvertently. Cropping with early ware potatoes is usually considered useful in controlling potato cyst nematodes because the crop is lifted before most cysts on the roots have matured. In some years the price of early potatoes falls sharply during June. Growers are then tempted to leave their crops to bulk during July and lift later as early main ware potatoes, thus allowing the cysts to mature and the population to increase. As the same fields often grow early crops every year, the build-up in population levels could be very rapid. Early crops should be lifted by the second week in June at the latest, leaving behind the minimum of crop debris, particularly roots, tubers and stolons.

On some farms, usually on smaller holdings or where 'good potato land' forms only a small proportion of the farm, soil sampling has enabled growers to select fields for potatoes from those with the lowest nematode densities. Catastrophic losses have been avoided because potatoes were not planted in the worst fields, but selecting fields only with low densities can reduce the potential cropping area of the farm. Maximising the cropping area by including fields with higher nematode densities can lead to a rapid increase in the overall level of the pest on the farm. The higher the potential yield of a field, compounded by such factors as soil fertility, manuring and farming skill, the larger the nematode population and the greater the crop loss which the farmer can accept. A particular difficulty may arise when it is necessary to bring fields known to be infested with potato cyst nematode into the potato rotation. The difficulty may be partly overcome by bringing fields into the new rotation in ascending order of nematode density. Resistant varieties and nematicides usually have a crucial part to play during the change-over period. Optimum rotation is stable for both high and low potential yields (page 44), so that the conclusions to be drawn from calculations based on various prices, yields, nematode densities and population changes are likely to be widely applicable. At any given level of fixed costs, too wide a potato rotation may be just as uneconomic as one that is too narrow and will usually result in a smaller income from the farm. Too narrow a rotation will be uneconomic because the increased potato area will not compensate for the yield losses caused by the nematodes.

With careful monitoring and sensible cropping decisions, an integrated control programme for potato cyst nematodes can be used for many years in some situations. However, a major problem has been experienced in some areas where Ro1-resistant varieties have been used. A series of ADAS surveys of potato cropping in the Isle of Ely, Cambridgeshire, showed how quickly growers adopted the resistant variety Maris Piper as the maincrop white-fleshed potato instead of the traditional variety, Majestic. The variety had a high yield potential and was just as acceptable to the market as Majestic. Introduced in 1969, Maris Piper had entirely replaced Majestic by 1975. From 1976 onwards, Maris Piper increasingly replaced King

Edward also. The variety was attractive to growers because agronomically and economically it was one of the best varieties to grow and because it was resistant to the predominant potato cyst nematode present in their fields — *G. rostochiensis* Ro1. Unfortunately *G. pallida* was also present, although initially only in small numbers. In these circumstances the over-frequent use of a variety that was susceptible to *G. pallida* led to a build-up in this species, so that in many places numbers of potato cyst nematode became almost as great as before Maris Piper was grown. This demonstrates that a single component of an integrated control programme cannot be used successfully alone for very long.

Varieties with the same gene for resistance, such as Maris Piper or Pentland Javelin, should not be grown very frequently or continuously because, if *G. pallida* is present, it will build up to damaging numbers within a few years. It was once thought that alternating resistant and susceptible varieties in a relatively short rotation, e.g. one potato crop every four years, would maintain *G. rostochiensis* Ro1 at an acceptably low level but enable it to compete successfully with *G. pallida* and other pathotypes of *G. rostochiensis* should they occur. However, recent work has shown that *G. pallida* is almost always capable of ousting *G. rostochiensis* in the long term.

In addition to decreasing nematode numbers, granular nematicides are a valuable aid to the grower in helping to minimise nematode damage and to level out fluctuations in yield loss due to potato cyst nematodes. Adoption of their use has been rapid, to the extent that they are often used when nematode levels are low or undetectable in soil samples. However, it has recently been found that in some UK soils such chemicals are degraded very rapidly and rendered ineffective. It is possible that this problem could become widespread through overuse of granular nematicides.

At present, a long interval between potato crops, or a very effective nematicide, or commonly both, are usually necessary in fields where susceptible varieties are grown, either from choice or because there are no varieties resistant to the potato cyst nematode present. The availability of varieties which are resistant to both species would give the grower more choice in planning crops, but the experience with Maris Piper suggests that such varieties should be used prudently.

Statutory regulations and soil sampling

Since 1973, safeguards against the spread of potato cyst nematodes with seed potatoes and other planting material have been obligatory in Great Britain to comply with the EC Directive on the control of these pests. Seed potatoes intended for marketing must be produced only on land on which no viable potato cyst nematode has been found as a result of an official soil examination. On land declared by notice to be infested, the growing of ware potatoes except under licence and the removal of any plants (including bulbs) for transplanting are also prohibited. Licences may be issued to grow potatoes, other than seed potatoes, on land under notice provided that: (i) ware potatoes are grown and lifted before 1 July in any year; or (ii) they are a variety resistant to the species or pathotypes of nematode found on the land; or (iii) the land has been treated with a nematicide or soil sterilant officially approved for use against potato cyst nematodes.

The restrictions on infested land will be lifted when viable potato cyst nematode is no longer found by a further official soil test. Applications for retesting will be accepted after an interval which varies according to the crop to be grown; the interval is greatest for the highest grade seed crops and smallest for ware crops. Further information may be obtained in England and Wales from the local office of the Ministry of Agriculture, Fisheries and Food and in Scotland from the Department of Agriculture and Fisheries for Scotland. The arrangements for advisory soil testing at the request of the farmer (usually done in consultation with an Agricultural Advisory Officer of ADAS) to assist in planning cropping are not affected by the statutory controls. Advisory soil testing will be used solely for advising the farmer on his nematode problems. Farmers are urged to continue to make the fullest possible use of ADAS in the interests of effective control of these serious pests.

Further reading

ADAS Leaflet P3061. *Potato nematodes*. Ministry of Agriculture, Fisheries and Food, London.

BROWN, E. B. (1976). Assessment of damage by nematodes, with economic considerations. *Annals of Applied Biology* **84**, 448–51.

BROWN, E. B. (1983). The relationship of potato yield with and without nematicide to density of potato cyst nematodes, *Globodera rostochiensis* and *G. pallida*. *Annals of Applied Biology* **103**, 471–6.

BROWN, E. B. and SYKES, G. B. (1983). Assessment of the losses caused to potatoes by the potato cyst nematodes, *Globodera rostochiensis* and *G. pallida*. *Annals of Applied Biology* **103**, 271–6.

COWTON, M. (1983). Integrated control of potato cyst nematode. *Twenty-third Annual Review of the Terrington Experimental Husbandry Farm, 1983*, pp. 16–18.

JONES, F. G. W. (1969). Integrated control of the potato cyst nematode. *Proceedings of the Fifth British Insecticide and Fungicide Conference, 1969*, **3**, 646–56.

JONES, F. G. W. (1970). The control of the potato cyst-nematode. *Journal of the Royal Society of Arts* **118**, 179–99.

JONES, F. G. W. and JONES, M. G. (1984). *Pests of Field Crops*. (3rd edition). London: Edward Arnold.

SOUTHEY, J. F. (Ed.) (1978). *Plant Nematology*. (3rd edition). GDI (previously Technical Bulletin No. 6) of the Ministry of Agriculture, Fisheries and Food, London. HMSO.

SHORT, J. L. (1984). Living with potato cyst nematode in the Fens. *Annual Review of the Arthur Rickwood Experimental Husbandry Farm, 1984*, pp. 10–16.

TRUDGILL, D. L. (1986). Yield losses caused by potato cyst nematodes: a review of the current position in Britain and prospects for improvements. *Annals of Applied Biology* **108**, 181–98.

WHITEHEAD, A. G., TITE, D. J., FRASER, J. E. and NICHOLS, A. J. F. (1984). Differential control of potato cyst-nematodes, *Globodera rostochiensis* and *G. pallida* by oxamyl and the yields of resistant and susceptible potatoes in treated and untreated soils. *Annals of Applied Biology* **105**, 231–44.

NEEDLE NEMATODES

Needle nematodes (*Longidorus* spp.) are commonly occurring ectoparasites. One species, *Longidorus leptocephalus* Hooper, feeds on potato roots growing below cultivation depth and reduces yield. Feeding by this nematode in the deeper layers of soil could be responsible for the poor growth of potatoes in the absence of other obvious causes.

STUBBY-ROOT NEMATODES

Nematodes of the genera *Trichodorus* and *Paratrichodorus,* also ectoparasitic species, transmit tobacco rattle virus (TRV), which produces an internal disorder of the potato tuber called spraing. Virus infection does not affect crop yield but reduces tuber quality in susceptible varieties. In some seasons crops can suffer severe loss, affected tubers being unacceptable for sale yet impossible to grade out.

Incidence of spraing

Stubby-root nematodes are restricted mainly to light, open-textured soils such as the sandy soils of the Vale of York, Norfolk and parts of the West Midlands. Not all populations of the nematodes carry TRV. The area of potatoes currently grown on spraing-infected soil is about 15 000 ha but only about 5 000 ha of susceptible varieties are likely to be at risk.

Migrating nematodes require adequate soil moisture to enable them to move between soil particles. Consequently, nematode activity and the incidence of spraing are influenced by seasonal weather factors, spraing being more common in wetter growing seasons. Regular crop irrigation, especially early in the season, can also increase the risk of the disorder if TRV and nematodes are present.

Crop damage

Tubers become infected with TRV when the skin is pierced by the mouth-spear of virus-carrying nematodes; most infection occurs soon after tuber initiation. When an infected tuber of a susceptible variety is cut open symptoms of spraing are seen as chestnut-brown lines, arcs or circles on the cut surface (Plate 2b). The symptoms do not increase in severity during crop storage and affected tubers remain sound in store. Less frequently, potato mop top virus, which is transmitted by the powdery scab fungus, also causes spraing-like symptoms.

TRV is rarely systemic in the potato plant and the current season's infection does not reach the foliage. Spraing-affected tubers usually produce healthy plants but occasionally some show foliar symptoms known as stem mottle. On these plants, affected stems are short and have crinkled, imperfectly formed and discoloured leaves. Tubers formed on stem mottle stems show secondary symptoms of spraing in the form of internal brown flecks.

Varietal susceptibility

Some potato varieties show symptoms of spraing in their tubers more readily than others. Pentland Dell, for example, is highly susceptible whereas Record is one of the least susceptible to damage. The National Institute of Agricultural Botany's recommended list of potato varieties gives a rating for spraing-TRV susceptibility and should be consulted when choosing a variety to be grown on fields with a history of the disorder.

Cultural control

Soils can be examined for the presence of the nematode vectors but it is not practicable to test these for TRV. However, 'spraing' soils are usually known from previous experience and, in these situations, highly susceptible varieties should be avoided.

TRV can persist in a population of the vector nematode for several years because the virus also infects some common weeds including chickweed and shepherd's purse. Seed transmission in weeds also maintains the presence of TRV in the soil. Effective weed control will therefore reduce the persistence of the virus.

Some crops grown in rotation with potatoes can help to reduce the incidence of spraing. Barley, for example, although a good host of *Trichodorus* spp. is not a host of TRV. The nematode loses its infectivity after feeding on barley and the incidence of spraing in potatoes declines as the number of preceding barley crops increases. Every effort must be made, however, to maintain good weed control.

Chemical control

Where a susceptible potato variety is to be grown on land with a history of spraing, the use of a granular nematicide will give some control of the nematode vector and reduce the incidence of the disorder. The nematicides aldicarb and oxamyl are currently recommended to reduce spraing symptoms on susceptible varieties. Granules are either broadcast pre-planting or applied in-furrow at planting, according to the manufacturer's instructions. Nematicide granules applied at or before planting for the control of potato cyst nematodes will also reduce the incidence of spraing.

Further reading

ADAS Identification Card 166. *Spraing (TRV) of potato*. Ministry of Agriculture, Fisheries and Food, London.

ADAS Leaflet P3061. *Potato nematodes*. Ministry of Agriculture, Fisheries and Food, London.

BRENCHLEY, G. H. and WILCOX, H. J. (1979). *Potato Diseases*. RPDI of the Ministry of Agriculture, Fisheries and Food, London. HMSO.

POTATO TUBER NEMATODE

The potato tuber nematode (*Ditylenchus destructor* Thorne) is an endoparasitic species which attacks the potato tuber. It used to be troublesome in the fenland areas of East Anglia, but nowadays infestations are rare. Invasion of the tuber occurs in the field and damage progresses during storage; the most serious losses occur when bulk stores such as clamps become moist.

Potato tuber nematode closely resembles the stem nematode (see page 52) and can only be distinguished from it by specialist microscopic examination. It differs from stem nematode, however, in that it lives only on the underground parts of plants and is less able to survive dry conditions. Breeding occurs continuously when conditions are favourable and there is an ample food supply; all stages (eggs, juveniles and adults) can be found together in an infested tuber.

Host plants

Crops

Apart from potatoes few other arable crops are likely to be seriously affected by this pest. It has been shown experimentally that mangels, sugar beet and carrots can be hosts, but attacks on these crops in the field have not yet been found in Britain. The only other host plant of commercial significance in Britain is bulbous iris. In practice, this is usually an entirely separate problem because iris bulbs and potatoes are unlikely to be grown commercially on the same farm. Potato tuber nematode has also been found damaging tulip bulbs, gladiolus and *Tigridia* corms, and the roots of lilac and hops, but it is not regarded as a serious pest of any of these plants.

Weeds

Corn mint (*Mentha arvensis*) is the chief weed host of potato tuber nematode in Britain. The nematode invades and multiplies in the creeping rhizomes of this weed, which, in some areas, determines whether the nematode can persist and become a serious pest. Infestations have also been found in the rhizomes of corn sowthistle (*Sonchus arvensis*), which probably plays a similar though less important part in maintaining infestations. Potato tuber nematode is unlikely to survive in a normal potato rotation in the absence of these weeds.

Tuber damage

A potato tuber heavily infested with this pest shows, typically, slightly sunken areas on the surface with cracked and wrinkled skin that is detached in places from the underlying flesh (Plate 2c). The decaying tissue, seen through the larger cracks, usually has a dry and mealy appearance and varies in colour from greyish to dark brown or black. The dry, spongy texture of infested tubers distinguishes the effects of tuber nematode from those of potato tuber diseases such as blight and dry rot.

In the early stages of nematode infestation however, none of these more obvious effects may be seen. The nematodes enter potato tubers through the lenticels or the eyes and multiply in small areas or pockets before there is any sign on the tuber surface. On peeling an infested tuber at this early stage, these pockets of infestation can be seen as small off-white spots in the otherwise healthy flesh. Later they enlarge and become darker and woolly in texture. The surrounding tissue rots as secondary organisms gain entry, and the skin dries, shrinks and cracks to give the typical appearance described above.

When stored dry, infested tubers gradually dry up and become mummified. There is little or no spread of infestation in store provided the tubers do not become wet. In moist conditions, however, the nematode attack progresses rapidly and bacteria and other secondary rotting organisms complete the decay of tubers.

Control

Potatoes from a crop known to have been affected by tuber nematode should not be used for seed because of the risk of spreading the pest into new areas.

The most effective means of controlling the pest in the field is by the destruction of its weed hosts. Mechanical cleaning operations are particularly important because the weed hosts are difficult to control with herbicides. The most practical method for the control of corn mint or corn sowthistle is by repeated cultivations aimed at exhausting the plants' rootstocks.

If potato tuber nematode is suspected in a crop, farmers should seek confirmatory diagnosis by ADAS. Lightly infested ware crops should preferably be sold immediately after harvest and not stored. More heavily infested crops are best used for stock feed, after boiling to kill the nematodes which could otherwise be spread about the farm with manure.

Further reading

ADAS Leaflet 372. *Potato tuber nematode.* Ministry of Agriculture, Fisheries and Food, London.

SOUTHEY, J. F. (Ed.) (1978). *Plant Nematology.* (3rd edition). GDI (replaces Technical Bulletin No. 7) of the Ministry of Agriculture, Fisheries and Food, London. HMSO.

STEM NEMATODE

Stem nematode (*Ditylenchus dipsaci*) (Kühn) Filipjev), like the closely related potato tuber nematode, is an endoparasitic species and is a destructive pest of many different crops. It can damage potatoes but infestations in Britain are very rare. The pest occurs as races or strains which differ in the range of host plants they attack. Investigations on the few infestations found in potato in Britain suggested that the common oat-onion race was present. However, as this race is so common, it is surprising that attacks on potato have not been found more frequently. The nematodes feed in plant tissue where they can breed continuously and are able to move through moist soil to invade other plants. If infested plants dry up, the stem nematodes become dormant and in this condition they often survive for several years, becoming active again only in the presence of moisture.

Where attacks have been noted in Britain, the nematode was responsible for causing stunting, twisting and swelling of the shoots, puckering of the leaves (Plate 2d) and a serious reduction in yield; nematodes were not found infesting the tubers. Damage to potatoes seems to be more common in some other parts of Europe, notably in the Netherlands and Germany where at least three races are known to multiply on the crop. There, tubers are attacked but the damage symptoms differ from those caused by potato tuber nematode in that the spongy decayed areas tend to penetrate further into the flesh of the tuber, and the skin covering these areas is less frequently cracked. Tubers damaged by stem nematode are thought to be less susceptible to secondary rots than those attacked by tuber nematode.

It is possible that races of stem nematode capable of attacking potatoes might be introduced into this country on imported tubers; any suspicious damage symptoms on incoming consignments should be carefully investigated.

ROOT-LESION NEMATODES

A root-lesion nematode (*Pratylenchus penetrans* (Cobb) Chitwood & Oteifa) has caused damage to potato crops on the Isles of Scilly. The nematodes were associated with lesions and rotting of the roots (Fig. 2a) and with poor patches in the crop similar to those caused by potato cyst nematodes. *P. penetrans* is only locally troublesome and on the mainland of England has been found chiefly in the south-west on light sandy soils, where mild climatic conditions seem to favour them, and only infrequently in the eastern counties. The three other species of root-lesion nematodes commonly occurring in outdoor soils in Britain are not known to damage potatoes.

Further reading

COMMONWEALTH INSTITUTE OF HELMINTHOLOGY. *Pratylenchus penetrans*. Descriptions of plant-parasitic nematodes, Set 2, No. 25.

ROOT-KNOT NEMATODES

Four species of root-knot nematodes (*Meloidogyne* spp.) occur outdoors in Britain. One of these, *Meloidogyne hapla* Chitwood, is fairly common on light soils, especially in the eastern counties. Although potato is one of its recorded host plants, this nematode has not yet been found on potato in the field in Britain. Attack of the growing crop by root-knot nematode could be recognised by the characteristic small galls that form on the fibrous roots.

Further reading

SOUTHEY, J. F. (Ed.) (1978). *Plant Nematology*. (3rd edition). GDI (replaces Technical Bulletin No. 7) of the Ministry of Agriculture, Fisheries and Food, London. HMSO.

Slugs

Slugs (and snails) belong to a much larger group of soft-bodied invertebrates known as molluscs. Members of this large group vary considerably in shape, size and habitat, but each has a muscular foot on which rests a mantle, which in turn is often covered by a shell. All molluscs, except some species of a group called gastropods, are entirely aquatic and, indeed, most gastropods are aquatic. Slugs are terrestrial gastropods without shells or with only small shells which may be internal. A clear-cut distinction between slugs and snails is arbitrary as all intermediate stages in shell reduction occur; in general, terrestrial gastropods that cannot withdraw into a shell are classed as slugs.

Description and habits

Slugs are soft bodied, unsegmented and slimy to the touch. They possess two pairs of retractable tentacles on the head and a distinctive mantle on the back, on one side of which opens a breathing pore. Other features which characterise different slug species include the degree of development of a ridge or keel along the tail, the presence or absence of a foot fringe, and the pigmentation of the skin, the sole of the foot and the mucus.

Beneath the first pair of tentacles is a transverse slit which opens into a cavity containing a rasping tongue or radula on which are arranged thousands of sharp teeth. This structure enables these pests to feed efficiently on a wide range of growing plants as well as on decaying plant material, fungi and carrion.

Slugs are active throughout the year whenever the temperature and moisture conditions are suitable, but during very dry weather, especially when it is frosty, they stop feeding and move down into the soil or shelter under debris. They are most active on still nights when the soil is wet and the atmosphere humid; wind and heavy rain decrease activity.

Slugs lay their eggs in clusters of up to 50 in the soil or in decaying organic matter (Plate 3c). The eggs are quickly killed by drought or frost unless they are protected by the warmth and damp provided by rotting vegetation and soil. The incubation period varies greatly: under warm spring conditions hatching may be complete within three weeks, whereas eggs laid in late autumn may not hatch until the following spring.

Apart from their size and lighter colour, young slugs resemble the adults. On hatching they first feed on organic matter and humus in the soil, but later their feeding habits vary. Most species will feed both underground and on the surface on a wide range of materials, including living and decayed parts of plants.

The species most harmful to potatoes are described below.

The **garden slug** (*Arion hortensis* Fér.) (Plate 3a) is a small, tough-skinned species which, when fully extended, rarely exceeds 30 mm in length. The body is semicircular in transverse section when contracted, with a bluntly rounded hind end and no trace of a keel. The foot fringe is narrow and often indistinct. The skin colour varies from brown to grey to blue-black with a lyre-shaped marking on the mantle and with banding of variable intensity along the body. Colour variations may represent separate sub-species. All forms secrete a yellow-orange mucus. The garden slug is most easily recognised by its bright orange or yellow sole. It is a major pest of agricultural land, showing a slight preference for the more calcareous or neutral soils. In some areas this species is nearly as common as the field slug (see below). The garden slug feeds both above and below ground. It has one generation a year and breeds mainly in mid- to late summer.

The **white-soled slugs** (*Arion circumscriptus* Johnst., *Arion silvaticus* Lohm. and *Arion fasciatus* (Nilss.)) are generally larger than the previous species, ranging from 30 to 50mm in length when fully extended. They are less heavily pigmented than the garden slug but possess the lyre-shaped marking and the dark lateral bands. Their bodies are more bell-shaped in transverse section when contracted and the hind end not quite so blunt, possessing a very slight keel. As their name suggests, they are readily distinguished from the garden slug in having strikingly white soles. Though considered to be of less economic importance than the garden slug, white-soled slugs can be more prevalent in some fields and at certain times. The members of the group are difficult to distinguish from one another and can only be identified with certainty when dissected; hence the relative distribution of the three species is not clearly understood. However, *A. fasciatus* is less common in the southern counties of England than *A. circumscriptus* or *A. silvaticus*. Breeding of white-soled slugs is thought to take place in the late summer and the autumn.

The **keeled slugs** are variable in colour but each possesses a distinct ridge or keel running along the back from the edge of the mantle to the tip of the tail, which is pointed. Mature specimens are much larger than the *Arion* spp. described above and, although mating and occasionally feeding above ground, these species are largely subterranean. Keeled slugs breed in the late autumn and spring.

Most serious damage to potatoes is caused by *Tandonia budapestensis* (Hazay) (Plate 3b). This species can be 50 to 60 mm in length when fully extended and then quite slender in appearance. When contracted, *T. budapestensis* tends to curl into a 'C' rather than a hump. Pigmentation is variable, ranging from yellowish-grey through brown to almost black. The breathing pore often has a black rim and the keel is dirty-yellow or orange. The pale sole has a characteristic darker central strip.

Milax gagates (Drap.), though similar in size to *T. budapestensis*, is more often dark grey or black with a darker keel. The sole is uniformly off-white. This species is more common in south-west England and Wales, where it can be damaging to potatoes.

Tandonia sowerbyi (Fér.) is the largest of the British keeled slugs and can be up to 75mm long when fully extended. The body is pale brownish-grey with darker speckles. The breathing pore has a pale orange rim. The keel is very prominent, usually yellow or orange, and characteristically crinkled when the animal is contracted. The sole is uniformly pale. *T. sowerbyi* secretes a thick, sticky and yellowish mucus unlike that secreted by the other two species, which is colourless.

The **field slug** (*Deroceras reticulatum* (Müll.)) is probably the most common British slug species and generally the most injurious. It is active even at low temperatures and, although able to feed below ground, is most active on the surface and on aerial parts of plants. Consequently, it is not such an important pest of potato as are the more subterranean species. Nevertheless, field slugs are often found in holed tubers and, when associated with other pest species, can cause considerable secondary damage. The field slug when mature is 35 to 50 mm in length. It is very variable in colour but often light grey or fawn with a dense pattern of darker flecks which give the body a speckled or reticulated appearance. When irritated this slug exudes a milky mucus. The tail is truncated and there is a short keel extending along the back, terminating before reaching the edge of the mantle. The field slug has two generations a year with a peak of breeding in April/May and another in September/October.

Damage

Slugs are serious pests of potatoes though perhaps of less economic importance than potato cyst nematodes or virus-carrying aphids. Slugs can spoil maincrop potatoes by penetrating the skin and excavating cavities, even large chambers, within the tuber (Plates 6d and 3d). Damage can be most serious in seasons when wet autumns follow mild, wet summers, especially when harvesting is delayed. Crops grown in heavier, more moisture-retaining soils are at most risk. Spoilage can occur at much lower population levels than would be considered economically damaging to cereals. Slugs may be carried into store, on or within infested tubers, where feeding continues. They may even feed on chits and seed tubers, but such damage is seldom important. Occasionally, slugs feed on the aerial parts of the potato plant, usually at night when the weather is humid and mild. They graze the stem and leaf petioles and eat irregular areas from the foliage (Fig. 9); slime is often present on damaged leaves. While this damage is unlikely to affect tuber growth or yield, it is an indicator of slug activity, which is important when timing molluscicide treatments (see below).

The garden slug and keeled slugs are the main slug pests of potato. Although the field slug is claimed to attack only tubers that are already damaged, it is capable of penetrating the skin of the tuber and certainly contributes considerably to tuber damage. Slug damage is sometimes confused with that caused by other pests such as cutworms and wireworms. However, cutworm damage (see page 84 and Plate 7a) more often occurs on light or medium soils (including peats) after hot, dry summers. Wireworms (see page 80) bore narrow holes straight into the tuber (Plate 6b) and do not create a wider chamber inside.

Control

The necessity to control any pest should be based on an assessment of risk and on the value of the crop. Public concern about the use of pesticides and possible effects on the environment should also be considered. Risk assessment will depend in the first instance on the farmer's own experience of slug damage on his land. Some measure of the active slug population may be obtained by observing feeding damage to weeds, volunteer cereals, etc. on the land before planting. Test-baiting is recommended. Small quantities of methiocarb pellets placed beneath a series of twenty 15-cm-square tiles placed across the field should be examined every three days. Slug counts at these baiting points will give a useful indication of surface activity and the degree of control that might be expected with a more general application of molluscicide.

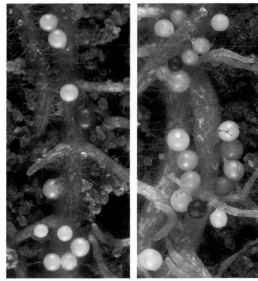

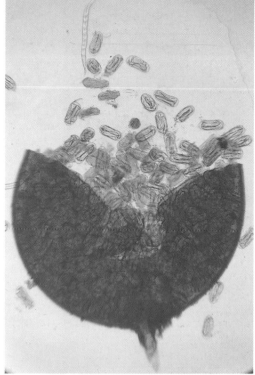

 1a ▲

Plate 1a. Females and brown cysts of potato cyst nematodes on potato roots (x10). *Left:* yellow potato cyst nematode. *Right:* white potato cyst nematode

Plate 1b. Ruptured potato cyst nematode cyst showing eggs and one free juvenile (x100)

Plate 1c. Potato crop showing patchy growth caused by potato cyst nematode infestation

1b ▲

▼ 1c

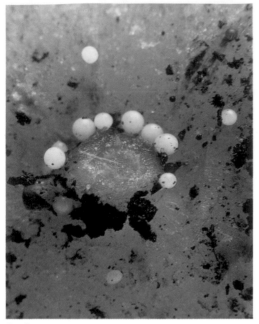

2a ▲

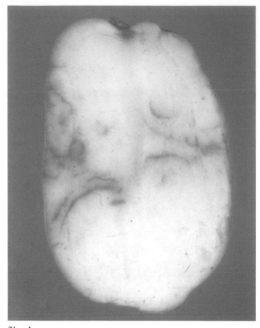

2b ▲

▼ 2d

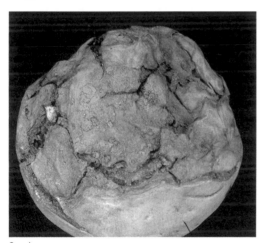

2c ▲

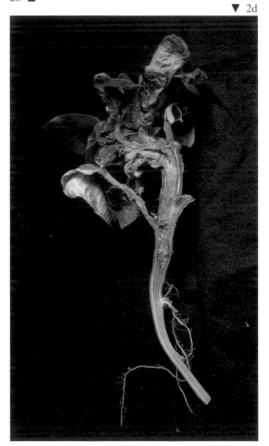

Plate 2a. Swollen females of potato cyst nematode on surface of potato tuber (x12)

Plate 2b. Potato tuber cut open to show symptoms of spraing caused by tobacco rattle virus

Plate 2c. Potato tuber showing external symptoms of attack by potato tuber nematode

Plate 2d. Stunting and distortion of potato plant caused by stem nematode. The stem has been cut open to show internal damage

Plate 3a. Garden slug (x5)

Plate 3b. Keeled slug
(*Tandonia budapestensis*)
(x2½)

Plate 3c. Egg cluster of a slug
(x2½)

Plate 3d. Potato tuber cut open
to show internal cavities caused
by slugs

▲ 3a

3b ▲

3c ▲

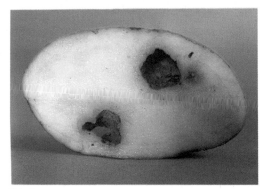

3d ▲

4a ▲

4b ▲

4c ▲

4d ▲

Plate 4a. Adult wingless and immature peach-potato aphids (x12)

Plate 4b. Adult wingless potato aphid with immature aphid at top (x12)

Plate 4c. Potato plant showing 'false top roll' caused by aphids

Plate 4d. Potato plant showing leaf roll caused by potato leaf roll virus

5a

Plate 5a. Glasshouse and potato aphids on sprout of chitting potato

5b ▲

Plate 5b. Common green capsid adult (x8)

Plate 5c. Capsid damage to potato foliage

▼ 5c

6a ▲

6b ▲

Plate 6a. Click beetle and wireworms (x2½)

Plate 6b. Potato tubers showing external and internal damage by wireworms

Plate 6c. Cockchafer grub on potato tuber showing chafer damage

Plate 6d. Potato tuber showing external damage by slugs

6c ▼

6d ▲

7a ▲

7b ▲

7c ▲

Plate 7a. Turnip moth caterpillar on potato tuber showing cutworm damage

Plate 7b. Garden swift moth caterpillar on potato tuber showing swift moth damage

Plate 7c. Ant damage to potato tuber

Plate 7d. Spotted millepedes on damaged potato tuber (x3)

▼ 7d

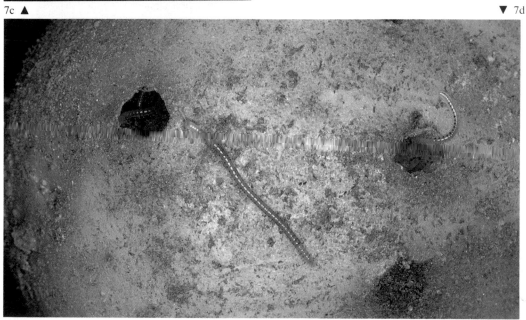

8a ▲

Plate 8a. Colorado beetle eggs on underside of potato leaf (x5)

Plate 8b. Colorado beetle larva (x4)

Plate 8c. Colorado beetle adults on potato plant showing early damage (x2)

8b ▼

8c ▼

Natural control

The weather and its influence on soil conditions can significantly affect the activity, proliferation and survival of slugs. During drought or prolonged periods of severe cold, egg laying is curtailed and those slugs that cannot reach the protection of deeper soil are killed. Although activity may be inhibited by short periods of cold or dry weather, it is quickly resumed when the temperature rises or the soil is moistened, even slightly, as by a heavy dew. Waterlogging will reduce slug numbers, particularly of those species which inhabit the upper layers of the soil. Slugs are occasionally eaten by birds, including the jackdaw, rook, lapwing and mallard. They are also eaten by frogs, moles, shrews, hedgehogs and various beetles, especially carabids.

Cultural control

In a situation where a slug attack is considered likely, it is possible to reduce slug numbers, or the extent of damage, without resorting to the use of molluscicides. Pre-planting cultivations, for example, can reduce slug populations by mechanical action which both kills the pest and reduces the size of soil spaces, thereby limiting the available protection from predators and from the extremes of cold or drought. However, it is not always possible to perform additional cultivations on heavy land where slugs are more common. Nevertheless, an attempt should be made to produce as fine a tilth as is practicable.

The risk to maincrop potatoes increases considerably during the autumn when conditions become more favourable to slug activity. Such damage can be checked by lifting the crop as soon as it matures. Unfortunately, in wet summers damage can be quite severe long before tuber maturity.

Potato varieties vary in their susceptibility to attack; this is, in some way, associated with biochemical factors such as starch content and/or the presence of secondary compounds such as glyco-alkaloids. Physical properties of the tuber, such as skin type, are also contributory factors. Hence, the choice of potato variety presents another means of cultural control. Known varietal susceptibilities in order of *increasing* susceptibility to slug attack are as follows: Pentland Ivory, Pentland Dell, Pentland Squire, Désirée, Record, King Edward, Pentland Hawk, Pentland Crown, Cara, Maris Piper.

Chemical control

For many years the chemical control of slugs has relied on pelleted bait formulations of metaldehyde or methiocarb. These baits are generally based on bran or wheat germ and treated with a water repellent to prolong pellet life. Pellets can be applied satisfactorily with many modern types of fertiliser distributor and air-assisted applicator or by custom-built low-ground-pressure vehicles. Pellets may even be broadcast by hand (wearing protective gloves) when treating small areas. Pellets are formulated to give an optimum number of baiting points when scattered 10–20 cm apart.

Metaldehyde poisons slugs by direct contact or by being ingested. Slugs seldom consume enough active ingredient to die immediately but are eventually immobilised and become vulnerable to predation and desiccation, particularly in dry conditions when exposed to sun and wind. Methiocarb is a stomach poison and less dependent on weather conditions for its effect. All baits are most effective when applied to the soil surface in mild, moist weather; heavy rain will reduce their effectiveness.

When slugs are active on the surface, spraying with copper sulphate may decrease slug numbers, provided the chemical is able to make direct contact with the pest.

Present chemical control methods rely for the most part on the slugs coming to the soil surface to feed on baits. Treatments applied in the spring, before planting, can help to prevent subsequent damage. Some control is possible with methiocarb pellets broadcast over the ridges in late July or August. Treatments applied later in the growing season, when slugs may already be feeding on tubers below the soil surface, will give little or no control. Remember that test-baiting can give a rapid indication of surface activity and the potential target for a molluscicide.

Molluscicidal pellets are harmful to humans, game and wild birds and mammals; they are also attractive to domestic animals and should be stored securely.

Further reading

ADAS Leaflet 115. *Slugs and snails*. Ministry of Agriculture, Fisheries and Food, London.

AIREY, W. (1984). The distribution of slug damage in a potato crop. *The Journal of Molluscan Studies* **50**, 239–40.

CAMERON, R. A. D., EVERSHAM, B. and JACKSON, N. (1983). A field key to the slugs of the British Isles. *Field Studies* **5**, 807–24.

GOULD, H. J. (1965). Observations on the susceptibility of maincrop potato varieties to slug damage. *Plant Pathology* **14**, 109–11.

PORT, C. M. and PORT, G. R. (1986). The biology and behaviour of slugs in relation to crop damage and control. *Agricultural Zoology Reviews* **1**, 255–99.

RAYNER, J. M., BROCK, A. M., FRENCH, N., GOULD, H. J. and LEWIS, S. (1978). Further experiments on the control of slugs in potatoes by means of molluscicidal baits. *Plant Pathology* **27**, 186–93.

WINFIELD, A. L., WARDLOW, L. R. and SMITH, B. F. (1967). Further observations on the susceptibility of maincrop potato cultivars to slug damage. *Plant Pathology* **16**, 136–8.

Aphids, leafhoppers and capsid bugs

Aphids, leafhoppers and capsid bugs belong to a large group of insects — the bugs (Hemiptera) — which have piercing and sucking mouthparts. The young, known as nymphs, closely resemble the adults except that they are smaller and lack fully developed wings. The group is subdivided into two according to wing characters. One subdivision contains several economically important families that feed on plant sap; of these, only aphids and leafhoppers are pests of potato in Britain. Capsid bugs are included in the other subdivision, which contains predators and blood suckers as well as plant feeders. Although most capsid species, like the potato capsid, feed on plant sap, some are predatory and therefore beneficial.

APHIDS

Aphids are the small, ubiquitous insects often referred to as greenfly or blackfly. There are numerous species which differ considerably in colour and life history. Some species are highly specialised and are found on one type of plant only, while others are capable of colonising a wide range of plants.

Aphids are characterised by having complex life cycles. Some species survive the winter in the egg stage, while others are more cold hardy and survive as adults or nymphs without any sexual stage; several species can overwinter in any stage. Those species which overwinter as eggs may require two types of host plant: a woody host on which fertilised females lay overwintering eggs and on which two or three generations of aphids may develop in the spring; and summer hosts (in this case potato) on which only unfertilised females that bear living young are found. The 'summer' females on potato may be winged (alates) or wingless (apterae), winged forms being produced in response to overcrowding or to a deterioration in food supply. Migration to the winter host is a response to decreasing day-length and lower temperatures in the autumn. The winged forms produced in the autumn leave the potato crop and fly to the winter host where they produce wingless egg-laying females. The latter are fertilised by winged males which have themselves migrated to the winter host from a summer host.

Aphids can cause yield loss to potato crops as a result of their feeding on sap and by the transmission of viruses from infected to healthy plants. Yield loss from aphid feeding is significant only when moderate to large numbers are present. In general, yield losses due to virus diseases are more serious than those caused directly by aphids.

Species

Four species of aphid occur commonly on potato foliage. These are the peach–potato aphid (*Myzus persicae* (Sulz.)), the potato aphid (*Macrosiphum euphorbiae* (Thos.)), the glasshouse and potato aphid (*Aulacorthum solani* (Kltb.)) and the buckthorn–potato aphid (*Aphis nasturtii* Kltb.). Other species occasionally found breeding on the foliage include the shallot aphid (*Myzus ascalonicus* Doncaster) and the violet aphid (*Myzus ornatus* Laing); the latter can occur in large numbers on senescing and blight-damaged foliage in late summer. The black bean aphid (*Aphis fabae* Scop.) occasionally forms small colonies on leaves at this time. These and other migrating aphid species which alight and feed on potato foliage without producing colonies may contribute to the spread of certain virus diseases. The bulb and potato aphid (*Rhopalosiphoninus latysiphon* (Davids.)) occasionally infests the stolons (underground shoots). Several of these species may occur on seed potatoes in store.

Descriptions and life histories

Peach–potato aphid

The peach–potato aphid is commonly found on potato and is regarded as the major aphid pest species on the crop. This is because it is the most efficient vector (i.e. carrier) of potato leaf roll virus (PLRV) and potato virus Y (PVY) — the most important aphid-borne viruses of potato. Several other potato viruses are transmitted by this aphid. Occasionally, severe leaf infestations develop and cause leaf necrosis.

The adult wingless aphid (Plate 4a) is medium-sized (1.4–2.6 mm long), oval and ranges from pale yellow-green to dark green. Immature winged aphids are often pink. Adult winged forms have a dark head and thorax and a green (sometimes pinkish) abdomen with a dark patch on the back.

This species can overwinter in the egg stage on peach and nectarine, but more commonly it overwinters as adult and immature stages on brassicas, beet and mangel clamps and many glasshouse and outdoor herbaceous plants, including common weeds such as annual nettle, groundsel and shepherd's purse. It also survives on seed potatoes in store. Winged forms migrate to a wide range of summer hosts including potato in May and June. Wingless aphids multiply on potato, reaching peak numbers from mid-July to early August. Further dispersal of winged aphids within and between potato crops may occur in late July and August in response to overcrowding, but generally numbers decline in late summer. Winged aphids later migrate to winter hosts.

Routine control measures are required against this species on seed crops. Choice of the most appropriate treatment is complicated by the widespread occurrence of moderate and high levels of resistance to insecticides. Control on ware crops is only necessary if populations are exceptionally large.

Potato aphid

The potato aphid is usually the commonest species found on potato. It can be extremely damaging in some years when large infestations cause the rolling and distortion of leaves known as 'false top roll' on the upper part of the plant. The potato aphid is an important vector of PVY. Although in Scotland this species is occasionally thought to be an important vector of PLRV, most populations transmit this virus poorly.

The adult wingless aphid (Plate 4b) is relatively large (2.5–4.0 mm long), spindle- or pear-shaped and green or pinkish-red with a dark longitudinal stripe along the middle of the back. The young are covered with a light dusting of waxy powder. Winged aphids have a yellowish-brown head and a green abdomen.

This species may overwinter in the egg stage on *Rosa* spp., but more usually it overwinters as adult and immature stages on many common species of weeds, including annual nettle, groundsel and shepherd's purse. Potato sprouts in store can become infested during the winter and spring. It migrates to a wide range of summer hosts, particularly potato and other Solanaceae, in May or June. Unlike other aphids which infest potato, this species tends to multiply on the flowers and shoot tips, producing false top roll symptoms when numerous.

Control measures are justified in years when infestations are large, i.e. exceeding five aphids per compound leaf. No insecticide resistance has been detected to date in field populations of this species.

Glasshouse and potato aphid

The glasshouse and potato aphid is often found on potatoes in the field but is rarely numerous. Therefore, in spite of its ability to transmit both PLRV and PVY, it is not regarded as an important pest of potato.

The adult wingless aphid is medium-sized (1.8–3.0 mm long) and pear-shaped. It is usually shiny yellow-green with a bright green or rust-coloured spot at the base of each siphunculus (tube at either side towards the hind end of the abdomen); uniformly dull green or greenish-brown forms are also found. Winged aphids have a dark brown head and thorax and a yellow-green abdomen, often with transverse dark bars or spots on the upper side.

This species is unusual in its ability to overwinter in the egg stage on many different host plants. Adults and immature forms can also overwinter on a wide range of plants in glasshouses and on sprouts of seed potatoes in store (Plate 5a), as well as plants such as annual nettle and foxglove outdoors. In the summer a very wide range of plants from different families are colonised. It is regarded as a common pest in glasshouses.

Control in the field is rarely justified, but seed potatoes in store may require treatment.

Buckthorn–potato aphid

This species is usually unimportant on potato, but epidemics were occasionally recorded in the years before aphicides were widely used on potato. It can transmit some of the non-persistent potato viruses including PVY and is an inefficient vector of PLRV.

The adult wingless aphid is small (1.1–2.2 mm long), rounded and bright yellow or yellow-green without distinctive markings. Winged aphids have a dark brown head and thorax with brown markings on the sides of the abdomen. This species overwinters in the egg stage on buckthorn, the eggs hatching in April. In June, winged aphids migrate to potato and other Solanaceae, and also to plants in the families Cruciferae and Polygonaceae.

Control measures are usually unwarranted on potato.

Bulb and potato aphid

The bulb and potato aphid is an occasional pest of seed potatoes in store, where it may cause direct damage by feeding on sprouts. It is also thought to be capable of spreading PLRV and PVY but is regarded as a relatively inefficient vector.

The adult wingless aphid (1.6–2.4 mm long) is shiny dark olive-green with a shiny dark shield covering most of the back. The antennae are long, as are the siphunculi, which are shiny black and very swollen. Immature stages are paler green.

Immature and adult forms overwinter on potatoes and bulbs in store and may live all year round on roots and aetiolated shoots of many outdoor plants. Sexual forms are unknown in this species.

Infestations found on potato in the field usually arise from the planting of infested tubers. Aphids multiply on the stolons and further development occurs in heavy, moisture-retaining soils. Colonies may appear above ground if infestations are severe.

Control measures are sometimes necessary on seed potatoes in store but not on field crops.

Other aphids

The **shallot aphid** may occur in small numbers especially after a mild winter. It can transmit PLRV but not PVY. The adult wingless aphid (1.4–2.1 mm long) is pale yellowish-brown or greenish-brown with long antennae, and siphunculi that are swollen towards their tips. Winged aphids have a dark head and thorax and a solid central dark patch on the upper side of the abdomen. Immature and adult aphids overwinter on strawberry and brassica crops, a wide range of common weeds, and onions and shallots in store. Sexual forms are unknown. Winged aphids migrate to a very wide range of summer hosts including potato in May and June. Control measures are not warranted on potato.

The **violet aphid** can infest potato crops and large numbers occasionally develop in late summer. Unlike other aphids this species may colonise the upper surface of leaves. Although it can transmit PLRV and PVY, it is an unimportant vector as few winged forms are produced on potato. The egg stage is unknown. The adult wingless aphid is small (1.0–1.7 mm long), oval, flattened and pale yellow or green with a pattern of dark dots or transverse streaks on the back. Winged aphids, which are slightly larger, have a black central patch on the back, with dark antennae, siphunculi and cauda (extended tip of the abdomen). The species colonises a very wide range of plants, overwintering as adults or immature stages in glasshouses and sheltered situations outdoors. Small numbers may migrate to potato crops in May–July. Control measures are not warranted.

Several other species of migratory aphids which do not colonise potato can transmit some viruses (e.g. PVY) when the aphid makes a short feeding probe of less than one minute while searching for its own host plant. The **leaf-curling plum aphid** (*Brachycaudus helichrysi* (Kltb.)) is an important vector of PVY in England and Northern Ireland. After overwintering on various *Prunus* spp., especially plum, damson and sloe, this aphid flies to a range of summer hosts belonging to the families Compositae and Boraginaceae. This migration occurs in June at a time when young potato plants are vulnerable to virus infection. The **bird-cherry** aphid (*Rhopalosiphum padi* (L.)), the **damson–hop aphid** (*Phorodon humuli* (Schrank)), and various *Aphis* spp. including the **black bean aphid** may also contribute to the spread of PVY in the UK.

Aphids and viruses

Many kinds of virus, some comprising several strains, may infect potato; of these at least 10 can be transmitted by aphids. Before the discovery of viruses, it had long been recognised that potato stocks in southern Britain declined in vigour more rapidly than those grown in the north. This difference was later attributed to the greater abundance and activity of aphid vectors which increased the spread of viruses in the south.

Primary and secondary infection

Primary infection occurs when aphids carrying viruses feed on healthy plants. Such infection spreads within the plants and into the developing tubers. Symptoms do not usually occur in the same season if plants are infected after tuber initiation. Secondary infection occurs in plants grown from infected seed tubers; this is more likely to result in serious yield reduction. In addition to causing losses in yield, virus diseases incur extra costs for the purchase of healthy seed or for insecticide treatment that may be applied to enable healthy seed to be produced.

Mode of virus transmission by aphids

Virus can be spread by aphids in one of two ways. For PVY, potato virus A (PVA) and some others, the aphid quickly acquires virus as it feeds on infected plants and can then quickly transmit it on moving to a healthy plant. Such acquisition and transmission take only a few minutes. This kind of virus spread is sometimes called stylet-borne (carried on the aphid mouthparts) or, since virus is quickly lost, non-persistent. By contrast, some viruses such as PLRV are located deep within the infected potato plant and are acquired only after long feeds of several hours. Transmission may occur only after a latent period of several hours. This long delay occurs because the virus must pass through the digestive system of the aphid and re-enter its saliva before transmission can occur. This is called circulative transmission or, since once acquired the virus is retained by the aphid for life, it is known as persistent transmission.

The mechanisms by which potato viruses are transmitted by aphids determine the kind of control measures which will be effective. Non-persistent virus spread occurs so rapidly that it cannot be effectively controlled by aphicide use; however, being lost by the vector so quickly, non-persistently transmitted viruses must spread from local virus sources. Vector aphids may be killed by aphicide deposits on potato plants before they can acquire and transmit persistent viruses. However, since these viruses persist in the aphid they can be brought from distant crops. A combination of aphicide use and isolation from virus sources is essential to prevent the introduction of both types of virus.

Aphid feeding behaviour and virus transmission

A winged aphid alights on hosts and non-hosts alike and may probe the leaf surface to determine its suitability as a host plant. These short testing probes are distinct from longer, deep, mainly intercellular intrusions required to penetrate and feed on the phloem cells. Even after probing a host species, an aphid may not settle and will fly to another plant. Non-persistent viruses which can be transmitted by aphid species that do not breed on potato may be acquired during such short exploratory probes. By contrast, persistent viruses are only acquired and transmitted by aphids which feed on the phloem cells of the plant. Aphid species differ greatly in their efficiency as vectors; the reasons for this are unclear.

Potato viruses

The two most important viruses affecting potato in the UK are potato leaf roll virus (PLRV) and potato virus Y (PVY).

PLRV is a persistent virus which can be transmitted only by aphids; the most important vector is the peach–potato aphid. Other recorded vector species are listed in Table 2. Primary infection with PLRV causes upward and inward rolling of the margins of the youngest leaflets, the incurving being more pronounced at the base of the leaflet than at its tip. Infected leaves may show a purplish discoloration. This symptom is easily confused with that caused by aphid feeding in the absence of virus (see page 71 and Plate 4c). A different symptom results when secondary (or tuber-borne) infection occurs. Affected plants develop characteristic rolling of the older, lower leaves (Plate 4d). The leaflets become tough and leathery due to the abnormal accumulation of starch and they rattle when shaken. The plant often has a stiff or 'staring' appearance, is frequently stunted and produces fewer and usually smaller tubers. It may be difficult to distinguish these symptoms from leaf rolling resulting from other causes.

Table 2. Aphid vectors of potato leaf roll virus and potato virus Y

Virus	Known aphid vectors (listed alphabetically)
Potato leaf roll virus (PLRV)	*Aphis nasturtii* *Aulacorthum circumflexum* *Aulacorthum solani* *Macrosiphum euphorbiae* *Myzus ascalonicus* *Myzus ornatus* *Myzus persicae* *Rhopalosiphoninus latysiphon*
Potato virus Y (PVY)	*Aphis fabae* *Aphis gossypii* *Aphis nasturtii* *Aulacorthum circumflexum* *Aulacorthum solani* *Brachycaudus helichrysi* *Cavariella pastinacae* *Macrosiphum euphorbiae* *Myzus certus* *Myzus ornatus* *Myzus persicae* *Phorodon humuli* *Rhopalosiphoninus latysiphon* *Rhopalosiphum padi*

PVY is a non-persistent virus; most of its strains are aphid transmitted. Many aphid species can transmit PVY (Table 2), but in the UK the most important vector is the peach–potato aphid. The symptoms caused by infection with PVY vary according to the variety affected. Generally, primary infection produces the symptom known as leaf drop streak: black streaks on the veins under the leaf extend until most lower leaves on the stem collapse and hang by a thread. Only the younger leaves may survive, showing a necrotic spotting and mosaic. Secondary (tuber-borne) infection results in a range of symptoms from mild mosaic to the crinkling of leaves known as rugosity or to necrosis and death. Plants with rugose mosaic symptoms usually remain stunted and pale. Symptoms produced by PVY infection are often termed severe mosaic as distinct from the mild mosaic symptoms produced by viruses such as the aphid-transmitted PVA and the mechanically transmitted potato virus X (PVX). However, a highly infectious strain of PVY, tobacco veinal necrosis virus (PVY^N), produces only a mild mosaic symptom but can cause loss of vigour and yield potential.

Other aphid-borne viruses are usually of little importance in comparison with PLRV and PVY. PVX, which is not spread by aphids, can produce more severe symptoms of mosaic when combined with PVY. Symptoms known as crinkle, caused by a combination of PVX and PVA, are sometimes found in stocks of the variety Désirée.

Factors affecting virus spread

The introduction of PLRV and PVY infection and their subsequent spread in a potato crop often depend on the survival and behaviour of populations of the peach–potato aphid. The variety of potato being grown and the maturity of the crop at the time aphids arrive are also important factors in determining the development of the diseases once they are introduced.

Sources of virus

An essential prerequisite for virus transmission is the presence of suitable sources of virus. Infected tubers planted as seed and the presence of infected volunteer plants within a potato crop are the most important virus sources. Both PVY and PLRV can also be introduced into completely healthy stocks by aphids flying in from infected neighbouring potato crops or from virus-infected crops growing in gardens or allotments. Severe peach–potato aphid infestations may also arise from adjacent overwintered brassica crops or mangel clamps. It is therefore unwise to plant potatoes in fields adjacent to such crops or to use unclassified seed tubers if it in intended to save once-grown seed, especially after a mild winter favouring aphid survival.

Aphid survival and migration

The proportion of the overwintering population which survives until the spring is dependent on the weather. Peach–potato aphid eggs laid on primary hosts in the autumn are cold resistant but, despite this, only 40–70 per cent of eggs may eventually hatch in the spring. Prolonged periods of low temperature probably reduce the viability of eggs more than any other factor. Similarly, the proportion of peach–potato aphid nymphs and adults which survives on secondary hosts during the winter is largely dependent on temperature; continued feeding during mild winters helps to maintain cold hardiness, particularly of adults. In general, the more aphids that survive the winter, the greater is the initial migration to potato crops in the spring. Virus diseases transmitted by the peach–potato aphid are more likely to occur in early-planted potatoes in years with a large aphid migration in the spring, whereas in years with a relatively small spring migration but a large summer immigration, virus diseases are more prevalent in crops planted late. In the cooler, less sheltered, northern parts of Britain fewer aphids survive the winter so the spring migration is reduced compared with southern areas.

Aphids can be found in flight over a considerable climatic range. The aphid's physiological state determines whether flight is prolonged and extensive. A high aphid population density favours the production of winged forms and also encourages them to take off, even when the macro-climate is unfavourable. Peach–potato aphids fly best in relatively windy weather (up to 11 km/h) in temperatures above 17°C. At wind speeds below 2.4 km/h, aphids can control their direction of flight. Winds over 5 km/h result in longer-range downwind dispersal. Warm, anticyclonic weather favours both aphid population increase and flight and, therefore, the spread of virus.

Aphid behaviour

The behaviour of winged aphids during the initial late spring migration and the later secondary summer migration is highly conducive to virus spread. Winged peach–potato aphids are very selective in their settling sites: having arrived in a potato crop they frequently leave it, perhaps after depositing some young nymphs, even though suitable settling sites are abundant. This behaviour allows further long-range aerial distribution, while low-level short flights allow a wide distribution of aphids within the crop. If a significant proportion of these aphids are carrying virus, a concomitant spread of virus within and between crops will occur. Wingless aphids produced by the winged migrants are much less important in virus transmission. Although peach–potato aphid nymphs are restless and may move up to 30 cm a day, the resulting localised spread of virus from the initial focus of infection is not significant.

Shelter

Aphids are likely to be more numerous in areas of the field where potato foliage is less dense, as well as in the more sheltered areas of fields such as shady areas in the lee of woodlands. Virus infection and spread will therefore be influenced by the size of such areas in potato fields.

Physiology of the potato plant

Potato varieties differ in their susceptibility to aphid colonisation and virus infection (Table 3). Some resistant varieties respond to virus infection by hypersensitive collapse, while others may be more tolerant. In addition, as plants mature they become less susceptible to infection and any infection that does occur may spread slowly within the plant. This is known as 'mature plant resistance'. Management practices which promote the rapid and early growth of the potato crop, such as the physiological ageing of seed pre-planting, will ensure that the plant is at a growth stage less susceptible to virus infection when aphids begin to migrate into the crop. Both the peach–potato aphid and the potato aphid are attracted to the green-yellow colour of ageing and senescing leaves as this is the cue for 'nutritionally correct' leaves.

Table 3. Field resistance of potato varieties to PLRV and PVY
(1 = poor resistance; 9 = good resistance)

Type	Variety	Resistance score	
		PLRV	PVY
First earlies	Arran Comet	4	2
	Maris Bard	5	8
	Pentland Javelin	4	8
	Ukama	5	6
	Ulster Sceptre	4	3
	Home Guard	4	4
Second earlies	Estima	4	2
	Marfona	4	4
	Maris Peer	4	3
	Wilja	4	2
Maincrops	Cara	5	7
	Désirée	4	7
	King Edward	5	2
	Maris Piper	4	4
	Pentland Crown	7	8
	Pentland Dell	5	4
	Pentland Squire	4	4
	Record	4	2
	Romano	3	8

Source: Recommended varieties of potatoes 1987. *NIAB Farmers Leaflet* No. 3

Natural enemies

The role of natural enemies in controlling the abundance and local spread of aphid populations in potato crops is not clear. However, natural enemies are often ineffective against virus vectors, which still cause losses even at low densities — relatively few aphids are required to introduce a damaging level of virus into a crop. Natural enemies are also not 'quick-acting' enough to prevent the spread of stylet-borne viruses such as PVY which can be inoculated into the potato plant in only a few seconds. Although numerous parasitoids attacking the peach–potato aphid have been recorded, actual levels of aphid parasitism in the field rarely exceed one per cent. This may be because the peach–potato aphid is a 'restless' species and is therefore relatively unattractive to natural enemies. Predators such as hover flies (Syrphidae), ladybirds (Coccinellidae) and green lacewings (Chrysopidae) are considered to be more effective than parasitoids in controlling the peach–potato aphid, particularly on primary hosts. Spectacular outbreaks of aphids can occur if predators are selectively removed, for example by broad-spectrum insecticides to which the peach–potato aphid may be resistant. In addition, entomophagous fungi are often destroyed by fungicides applied to the potato crop.

Aphids and seed potato production

The potato crop is unique in that large quantities of seed tubers are required for planting, typically 2.6–5.0 tonnes/hectare. Approximately 10 per cent of the world's potato production is used for seed tubers. Ideally, these tubers should be produced at locations well away from ware production areas and under specific phytosanitary conditions, thus avoiding the build-up or spread of serious pests and diseases. One of the major reasons for applying these restrictions in the UK is the need to produce seed stocks with an acceptably low level of virus infection; aphid-transmitted viruses are particularly important in this respect.

Classification of seed potatoes

All seed potatoes marketed in England and Wales must be classified under seed potato schemes operated in the UK (Table 4) or similar schemes in the EC, or by other countries growing seed in acceptable circumstances (Seed Potato Regulations 1978). Classification

Table 4. Classes of seed potato produced in the UK

EC category	Class
	VTSC (Virus-tested stem cutting) generations 1 and 2
	SE (Super Elite) generations 1, 2 and 3
BASIC SEED (entry grades for further classified seed production)	E (Elite)
	Class A (N. Ireland)
	AA
CERTIFIED SEED (not accepted for classified seed production)	CC

Table 5. Disease tolerances at growing-crop inspections in England, Wales and Scotland (percentage infected plants)

Disease	Basic seed				Certified seed
	VTSC	SE	E	AA	CC
Severe virus					
Leaf roll	0	0.01			
Severe mosaic	0	0.00	0.1	0.25	2.0
Tobacco veinal necrosis virus	0	0.00	0.0		
Mild mosaic	0	0.05	0.5	1.0	5.0
Black leg	0	0.25	0.5	1.0	2.0

ensures that seed is true to variety, free from notifiable pests and diseases and of a reliable standard of health.

Apart from varietal purity and authenticity, virus disease is a prime concern of seed classification. Basic seed (suitable for further seed production) is required to carry less than 4 per cent virus infection, and certified seed less than 10 per cent severe virus. To be reasonably certain of achieving these standards, allowance must be made for virus spread which remains undetected during the season of the inspection. For this reason, growing-crop inspection tolerances of virus are very low (Table 5). In most seasons very high standards of seed potato tuber health are achieved.

Production of home-saved seed

The Seed Potato Regulations prohibit the sale of non-classified seed. However, farmers can save seed from their crops for their own use. Home-saved seed is often a useful by-product of maincrop ware production in the form of small tubers or greens etc. graded out of ware. A major disadvantage is the risk of virus infection. However, the advantages, which include low cost and seed acclimatisation, are considerable. Seed-sprouting under controlled conditions in store is particularly advantageous where the intended seed crop is to be planted on heavy land which does not allow early planting, as this encourages the potatoes to bulk early. The haulm can then be burnt off before there is a late aphid build-up.

Varieties highly susceptible to virus (Table 3), particularly to PVY, are not suitable for home-saved seed in virus-prone areas.

Cultural control of aphids in seed crops

To ensure that the stringent tolerance levels for aphid-transmitted viruses in classified seed potatoes are achieved, it is essential that effective control measures are applied against aphids in the growing crop and, if necessary, in store. Ideally, equally strict attention to aphid control should also be paid in the production of home-saved seed. Chemical control should form the basis of aphid control programmes (see page 72). However, chemicals should preferably be used in conjunction with cultural control techniques (see below). This approach will remove or isolate sources of virus and help to keep the initial level of aphid infestation and any subsequent population build-up to a minimum. The likely effectiveness of the chemical control programme will thus be greatly enhanced.

Class of seed

The health of the initial stock is crucially important. Health standards of stocks intended for seed production should be higher than would normally be considered adequate for ware production. Basic seed must be used and, for virus-susceptible varieties, this should be of at least Super Elite quality (Table 4). The seed should be planted as early as possible to ensure that crop maturity is reached before aphid populations have built up to peak levels. Inferior quality seed should not be planted within 50 m of good new stock.

Location

Fields on the outskirts of towns or in villages and sheltered fields close to buildings or woods should be avoided as they are prone to colonisation by virus-carrying aphids. Windswept, exposed fields provide the best locations for seed production as they do not favour aphid immigration or breeding. Virus spread is greater at the edges of crops and in sparse plant stands. Large areas of potatoes therefore give better prospects for healthy seed than small areas. Home-saved seed should preferably not be taken from headland rows. Potatoes of poorer health should not be planted in the same field as, or in fields immediately adjacent to, high quality stock intended for seed; volunteer plants must be destroyed and fields with large numbers of them should be avoided.

Crop inspection and roguing

Growing-crop inspections in conjunction with roguing are essential in seed production, both to maintain varietal purity and to prevent the spread of disease. With aphid-transmitted viruses, if secondary symptoms from infected tubers appear before aphids become active, roguing is an effective and worthwhile technique. This is normally the case in high-grade seed-producing areas. However, roguing is less effective in lowland or southern areas, where aphids are often active before roguing is possible. Some virus spread occurs in such crops before infected plants become apparent and can be rogued out. For home-saved seed, the criteria for seed classification should be used as a guide. If the initial stock falls below the accepted standard or if primary symptoms are readily found, seed should not be taken. ADAS provides a virus-testing service for growers wishing to produce home-grown seed.

Haulm destruction

Early destruction of haulm limits the exposure of the crop to aphid colonisation and breeding and therefore to virus infection. Burning off with chemicals by specified dates is a requirement of seed potato classification in the higher classes and where substantial virus infection is apparent at inspection. In crops grown entirely for seed, the timing of haulm destruction will usually be determined by the size of the tubers. The earlier this is done, the less is the risk of severe virus infection. For crops entered for classification, a time limit for haulm destruction will be set, where necessary, by the authorities.

Direct damage by aphids

The prevention of virus introduction into seed crops is the most important function of aphid control programmes on potatoes. Strict attention to aphid control is therefore not a major concern of the ware grower. However, a moderate or heavy infestation of aphids in maincrop potatoes can damage the haulm by direct feeding to such an extent that appreciable yield losses occur. Average losses of 2.5 tonnes/hectare are fairly common, particularly in eastern England where aphid populations are often larger than elsewhere. Such losses are less likely in northern or western counties or in Wales. The yield loss is likely to be particularly severe if peak aphid numbers occur when the tubers are bulking in late July and August. Individual fields and each variety should be checked for large aphid populations at this time as aphid build-up can vary considerably within relatively small areas. Control measures can then be applied where necessary (see below).

False top roll

Small infestations of aphids can cause moderate yield losses by removal of water and nutrients from the plant. Aphid saliva also contains polyphenol oxidase enzymes, which may interfere with the plant's physiology. However, large infestations of the potato aphid developing on the top leaves of the potato plant can result in the disorder known as 'false top roll' (Plate 4c). Initial symptoms are pale green spots on young leaves, followed soon after by an upward rolling of leaf margins around the midrib. The leaf margins also become violet and necrotic. Only the upper leaves are affected. The symptoms are usually seen in a limited area of the crop at first, but they can quickly spread over the whole field. Photosynthesis in affected leaves is inhibited by impaired phloem transport and the subsequent accumulation of carbohydrate in the leaves. The tuber yield of affected plants can be decreased by 10–50 per cent.

Symptoms of false top roll can be confused with those caused by black leg or drought. They can also be confused with symptoms caused by PLRV, making the inspection of crops entered for seed classification difficult. However, false top roll is usually seen earlier in the year (late June/early July) than PLRV symptoms; close inspection of the crop will also reveal the presence of many live aphids, parasitised aphids and/or cast aphid skins. Also, the distribution of false top roll within the field is usually patchy, rather than occurring in isolated plants or rows as often happens when the problem is caused by the planting of virus-infected tubers. New leaves produced after the removal of aphids from plants affected by false top roll grow normally, but leaves already affected do not recover.

Potato varieties differ in their susceptibility to false top roll. Although it will occur to some extent in most varieties, Désirée and King Edward are usually the most severely affected.

Other types of direct damage

Occasionally, very severe infestations of the peach potato aphid occur and the leaves can be completely killed by the massive numbers of aphids present. False top roll symptoms are not seen when peach–potato aphid is the dominant species in the infestation as this aphid tends to colonise the older, senescing leaves at the base of the potato plant.

Chemical control

Aphids on seed potatoes in store

The peach potato aphid, the potato aphid, the glasshouse and potato aphid and the bulb and potato aphid can all colonise the sprouts of seed potatoes in store (Plate 5a). In addition to the serious damage they cause by feeding on the sprouts, which can sometimes be completely destroyed, all are capable to a greater or lesser extent of spreading virus. Aphid control in potato stores is therefore well worth while. Aphids can gain access to the store by flying in during the autumn. The bulb and potato aphid is usually introduced on tubers that have been infested in the field. Weeds in the store can also act as aphid sources and should therefore be destroyed. When ware growers receive a delivery of new seed, they should check the tubers for aphids and try to isolate basic from once-grown seed within the store to minimise the risk of virus spread.

Potato stores should be fumigated in the autumn once aphid flights have ceased (about mid-November) and subsequently checked regularly for any signs of reinfestation as a few survivors can multiply rapidly once conditions warm up. Fumigants are a convenient and effective method of control provided that a temperature above 15°C can be achieved for the duration of the fumigation and that the store is relatively gas tight. One product containing nicotine shreds is specifically recommended for the control of aphids in potato chitting houses. Other products containing nicotine shreds and some smokes containing gamma-HCH or pirimicarb have a general recommendation for aphid control in any protected environment. The use of a dimethoate spray applied by a hand lance with a long extension is recommended for the control of bulb and potato aphid in chitting houses.

Aphids in seed crops

Limiting the spread of aphid-borne viruses is easier to achieve in the traditional seed-growing areas of northern England and Scotland, where fewer aphids survive the colder winters and the main aphid migration to potato crops usually occurs later than in the rest of the UK. For growers of basic and once-grown seed outside these 'favoured' areas there is still scope for reducing virus spread by cultural means (see above), but in most crops some form of chemical control will be required, both to limit virus introduction and to prevent its spread within the crop.

Insecticide granules applied at planting (Table 6) can give useful early protection against the introduction of PLRV. For example, studies on the peach–potato aphid have shown that when potatoes are treated with the systemic carbamate insecticide aldicarb, a minimum of three hours' exposure is required for aphid mortality to reach 50 per cent. Although this is too slow for complete prevention of primary virus infection with either persistent (e.g. PLRV) or

Table 6. Insecticides recommended for the control of aphids on potato

Chemical	Chemical group
Granules applied in-furrow at planting	
aldicarb (S)	carbamate
disulfoton (S)	organophosphorus
phorate (S)	organophosphorus
thiofanox (S)	carbamate
Sprays applied to the growing crop	
demeton-S-methyl (S)*	organophosphorus
dimethoate (S)*	organophosphorus
heptenophos (S)+ deltamethrin	organophosphorus + synthetic pyrethroid
malathion†	organophosphorus
oxydemeton-methyl (S)*	organophosphorus
pirimicarb*	carbamate
thiometon (S)*	organophosphorus

(S) = Systemic insecticide

* Some products containing these chemicals are approved for aerial application

† Ware crops only

NOTE: The granular insecticide/nematicide oxamyl, when applied for potato cyst nematode control, will also reduce early aphid attacks.

non-persistent (e.g. PVY) viruses, the surviving aphids are thought to be inefficient vectors because of their reduced ability to fly and probe further plants. Secondary within-crop virus spread is, therefore, greatly reduced. Virus levels in crops can be reduced by 50–75 per cent by the use of granules at planting. However, depending on soil type and soil moisture, granules are only effective for up to eight weeks after planting. Thus regular spray treatments are likely to be necessary from mid or late June onwards to supplement the granule application. Where granules have not been used, regular spraying should start at about 80 per cent crop emergence or when warnings of aphid migrations to potatoes have been given by ADAS. Aphicide sprays are often required before the first blight spray is due, but later treatments can be tank-mixed with blight fungicide applications (providing the chemicals are compatible) to avoid excessive wheeling damage and other application costs. Aphicide sprays should then be repeated at 10–14 day intervals and continued until two to three weeks before haulm destruction. The earlier treatments are likely to be more effective in reducing virus spread. Repeated use of some chemicals, particularly organophosphorus insecticides, can result in rapid selection for highly resistant forms of the peach–potato aphid which would not be controlled by the later treatments.

A range of chemicals can be applied as foliar sprays to control aphids on potatoes (Table 6). Demeton-S-methyl and oxydemeton-methyl are the most effective of the organophosphorus insecticides and should prevent reinfestation for at least 10 days. The carbamate insecticide pirimicarb is also effective but lacks persistence; it is, however, the only chemical which allows the majority of beneficial insects to survive, so reducing the risk of a late infestation. All insecticides, particularly organophosphates such as dimethoate and thiometon, may be ineffective where highly resistant strains of the peach–potato aphid occur (see below).

The spread of the non-persistent virus PVY in seed potato crops is difficult to prevent by using insecticides. This is because PVY can be acquired and transmitted within minutes. Most currently available insecticides do not kill aphids fast enough to prevent such transmission. Also, there is evidence to suggest that slow-acting insecticides may even increase the spread of PVY because they render the plant distasteful to aphids, causing them to move about and probe more plants, thus enabling PVY to be transmitted to more plants. However, recent experimental work has shown that lethal and sub-lethal doses of many pyrethroid insecticides can decrease the transmission of PVY because the aphids become hyperactive (and therefore less likely to probe) as soon as they arrive on the plant. The effect is less marked in aphids which are resistant to organophosphorus (and to some pyrethroid) insecticides. The prospects for the exploitation of this effect are limited at present as only one product with a pyrethroid component is currently available for use on potato for the control of aphids (a mixture of the systemic organophosphorus compound heptenophos and the pyrethroid deltamethrin).

Prevention of direct damage to ware crops

The use of insecticide granules at planting is worth while only in years when aphids arrive early. They should, therefore, be applied only when early aphid migration is predicted. It is not necessary to apply routine aphicide sprays to prevent direct aphid damage to ware maincrop potatoes. However, a field-by-field assessment of the aphid population should be made when the tubers start to bulk. Ideally, a random sample of 30 true leaves (10 top, 10 middle and 10 lower leaves) taken from across the whole field (not just the headlands) should be examined and the aphids counted. Current recommendations are that, if an average of more than five aphids per true leaf can be found at any time during the early stages of tuber bulking, a single insecticide spray application will give a worthwhile yield response. A repeat treatment is unlikely to be necessary. Suitable chemicals are the same as those listed for the control of aphids on seed crops (Table 6). The use of a specific aphicide like pirimicarb will help to maintain an effective population of natural enemies in the field.

Aphid resistance to insecticides

Populations of the peach–potato aphid have developed resistance to organophosphorus (OP), pyrethroid and carbamate insecticides. Aphids achieve this resistance because their bodies contain large amounts of a carboxylesterase enzyme which enables them to overcome the toxic effect of the insecticide by rapidly breaking it down (OPs and pyrethroids) or by removing it (carbamates). This important attribute affects the control of the peach–potato aphid, particularly in seed potato crops where insecticidal treatments are applied regularly. No other species of aphid commonly found on potato shows resistance to insecticides at the present time.

The actual levels of resistance found vary from one aphid population to another. For practical purposes, there are three levels of resistance:

S – aphids controlled by all aphicides
R1 – aphids not easily controlled by OP insecticides
R2 – aphids not controlled at all by OP insecticides and not easily controlled by carbamate insecticides.

A further level of resistance (R3) has also been identified; such aphids are totally resistant to all OP insecticides and to carbamates. However, R3 aphids are rare in field crops at present, though they are commonly found in glasshouses. Mixed populations containing individual aphids with different levels of resistance are common. Cross-resistance to pyrethroid insecticides occurs in R1, R2 and R3 aphids.

Surveys have shown that S and R1 aphids are common throughout Britain, but R1 aphids are particularly numerous in eastern England where insecticide usage is more intense. Susceptible (S) aphids are relatively uncommon in eastern counties. R2 aphids are usually found in appreciable numbers on potato in Scotland and the north-east of England, and only occasionally in the rest of England and in Wales. However in 1986, more R2 aphids than usual were found in the Midlands and East Anglia. There is no evidence to suggest that insecticide pressure alone accounts for the relatively high incidence of R2 aphids in the north or elsewhere. Although seed potato crops are more intensively sprayed with insecticides than are ware crops, no differences have been found in the proportions of R2 aphids in ware and seed crops. Some circumstantial evidence suggests that high levels of resistance could be linked to cold hardiness in aphids, but recent experimental evidence does not support this view. Another suggestion is that certain biotypes of peach–potato aphid favour potato as a host crop in the north-east and that this preference is associated with high carboxylesterase activity.

High levels of resistance should be suspected if:

(1) the more potent OP insecticides (e.g. demeton-S-methyl, oxydemeton-methyl) fail to kill the smaller aphids on lower leaves within a week; or

(2) infestations develop soon after emergence where crops have been treated with phorate or disulfoton granules (assuming soil conditions have been damp enough for proper uptake of the chemical).

Some control of R2 aphids can be achieved using pirimicarb and/or by treating the crop with aldicarb or thiofanox granules at planting. R1 aphids can be controlled at least partially by using potent OP insecticides such as demeton-S-methyl or oxydemeton-methyl and certainly by carbamates. It is most important that the insecticide is applied at the manufacturer's recommended rate and, for sprays, in the correct volume of water. Resistance problems may otherwise be compounded, particularly if repeated applications of chemicals such as dimethoate are applied at reduced rates, e.g. in a tank-mix with blight fungicides. Dimethoate will not control R1 or R2 aphids and may actually cause an increase in the aphid population because of the selective removal of beneficial insects.

Insecticide application methods

Granules

Granular formulations of insecticides are applied in-furrow at planting. A granule applicator which meters granules into the soil at the required rate is attached to the planter, ridger or coverer, with the discharge tubes positioned in such a way that the granules fall in a band at the base of the furrow before earthing up. Accurate placement of granules is essential. Recommended rates of chemical vary according to soil type and the duration of aphid control required. Careful and regular attention to the calibration of granule applicators is necessary to avoid over- or under-dosing.

Foliar sprays

Aphicide sprays are most commonly applied to potato crops by conventional tractor-mounted or trailed hydraulic crop-sprayers and are normally applied in 200–400 litres of water/hectare. The larger volumes of water are necessary later in the season after the haulm meets in the row or where the crop canopy is dense, in order to ensure that some chemical penetrates the foliage. This is particularly important for the control of peach–potato aphids, which are often found on the lower leaves. Water volumes as great as 1000 litres/hectare are recommended for some products. As with granule applicators, sprayer calibration is very important.

Tram-lines are widely used as a method of matching swath widths, thus helping to ensure that the correct dose of insecticide is applied to the whole crop as well as reducing crop damage through excessive wheelings. Yield losses of up to 1.25 tonnes/hectare can be caused by wheeling damage.

Some aphicides can be applied as sprays from the air (Table 6), using either a fixed-wing aircraft or a helicopter. Chemicals are applied in much reduced volumes of water (usually 30–50 litres/hectare); the downwash from the aircraft aids spray penetration into the crop canopy. Great care is required to avoid spray drift on to other crops. The main advantage of aerial application is the lack of wheeling damage to the crop; this saving in crop damage can easily compensate for the increased cost of application.

Future developments

Plant breeding

Plant breeders are trying to produce commercially acceptable varieties with full or partial resistance to aphids and/or viruses. For example, studies in Scotland have shown that the potato varieties Pirola and Corinne show good resistance to PLRV and PVY because of specific physiological traits within the plant. Physical characteristics such as the degree of leaf hairiness are also being examined as a means of making potatoes less attractive to aphids.

Chemicals and application methods

There is considerable interest in the use of mineral oils either alone or in conjunction with insecticides for preventing or reducing the transmission of aphid-borne viruses, particularly non-persistent viruses such as PVY. Other novel chemical approaches such as the use of aphid alarm pheromones are also being studied. Improving spray coverage and penetration by using electrostatic sprayers is also being investigated. Applying 'side-bands' of insecticide granules into potato ridges seven to eight weeks after planting, in order to provide effective aphid control when it is most required, has also provided worthwhile results.

Biological control of aphids

The use of entomophagous fungi to control aphids is perhaps the biological control method most likely to result in significant progress. Sprayable formulations of fungi (myco-insecticides) are already available for aphid control under glass in the UK and may one day be suitable for use outdoors. This approach would necessitate the use of selective fungicides on the potato crop or the development of strains of fungi resistant to commonly used fungicides. Attempts could also be made to enhance natural fungal infections by cultural manipulation.

Further reading

ADAS Booklet 2388. *Control of diseases of potatoes.* Ministry of Agriculture, Fisheries and Food, London.

ADAS Identification Cards 120–128. *Potato, beet and brassica aphids.* (Nos 121–128 deal with species on potato.) Ministry of Agriculture, Fisheries and Food, London.

ADAS Identification Cards 151–170. *Potato diseases and disorders.* (Nos 163 and 164 deal with PLRV and PVY respectively.) Ministry of Agriculture, Fisheries and Food, London.

ADAS Leaflet 139. *Potato virus diseases.* Ministry of Agriculture, Fisheries and Food, London.

ADAS Leaflet 575. *Aphids on potato.* Ministry of Agriculture, Fisheries and Food, London.

BLACKMAN, R. L. and EASTOP, V. F. (1984). *Aphids on the World's Crops: An Identification and Information Guide.* Chichester: John Wiley & Sons.

EMDEN, H. F. van, EASTOP, V. F., HUGHES, R. D. and WAY, M. J. (1969). The ecology of *Myzus persicae. Annual Review of Entomology* **14**, 197–270.

FOSTER, G. N. (1986). Effects of two insecticidal spray programmes on aphids and the spread of potato leafroll virus. *Tests of Agrochemicals and Cultivars* No. 7 (*Annals of Applied Biology* **108,** Supplement) pp. 24–5.

FURK, C. (1986). Incidence and distribution of insecticide-resistant strains of *Myzus persicae* (Sulzer) (Hemiptera: Aphididae) in England and Wales in 1980–84. *Bulletin of Entomological Research* **76,** 53–8.

GIBSON, R. W., RICE, A. D. and SAWICKI, R. M. (1982). Effects of the pyrethroid deltamethrin on the acquisition and inoculation of viruses by *Myzus persicae. Annals of Applied Biology* **100,** 49–54.

HARRIS, K. F. and MARAMOROSCH, K. (Eds) (1977). *Aphids as Virus Vectors.* New York: Academic Press.

RADCLIFFE, E. B. (1982). Insect pests of potato. *Annual Review of Entomology* **27,** 173–204.

VEEN, B. W. (1985). Photosynthesis and assimilate transport in potato with top-roll disorder caused by the aphid *Macrosiphum euphorbiae. Annals of Applied Biology* **107,** 319–23.

LEAFHOPPERS

There are four species of leafhopper that attack potatoes, but they are seldom economically important. Leafhoppers (family Cicadellidae) are small and narrow, about 5 mm long, green or yellow; when disturbed they fly ('hop') from plant to plant. The green leafhoppers (*Edwardsiana flavescens* (F.) and *Empoasca decipiens* Paoli) are common hedgerow insects. They feed on the underside of leaves where they cause pale speckling and yellowing of the foliage; in severe attacks the leaves turn brown, wilt and die ('hopper burn'). Similar symptoms are caused by the potato leafhoppers (*Eupterycyba aurata* (L.) and *E. jucunda* (Herr.-Schäff.)), both of which are also common in hedgerows, especially those in which alder is growing. These leafhoppers do not transmit plant viruses in Britain. In North America, leafhoppers are the vectors of potato yellow dwarf virus, but fortunately this virus is unknown in Britain. Although the leaf-spotting caused by leafhoppers is very common, it is seldom worthy of insecticidal treatment.

CAPSID BUGS

Several species of capsid or, more correctly, mirid bugs (family Miridae) are frequently found on potato foliage. Some are chiefly predatory on aphids and other small insects. Two species which commonly cause damage to potato leaves and stems are the potato capsid (*Calocoris norvegicus* (Gmel.)) and the common green capsid (*Lygocoris pabulinus* (L.)) (Plate 5b). Other capsid bugs of minor importance as pests of potato are the tarnished plant bug (*Lygus rugulipennis* Popp.), the slender grey capsid (*Dicyphus errans* (Wolff)) and *Halticus saltator* (Fourcroy).

Both the potato capsid and the common green capsid overwinter in the egg stage on woody or succulent hosts including shrubs and hedgerow and fruit trees. The nymphs feed in spring on a range of herbaceous plants before migrating to potato crops in June or July. Adult bugs return to woody plants to lay eggs in August. The tarnished plant bug differs in that it overwinters in the adult stage under dead leaves and litter.

Damage

On potato, young leaves and stems are punctured near the growing points and a toxic saliva is injected into the plant tissues. Reddish-brown necrotic lesions develop around the point of injection and, as the leaf grows, it becomes puckered (Plate 5c). Affected tissues around the lesions subsequently collapse leaving ragged holes (Fig. 7). Complete defoliation and stem collapse may occur when attacks are severe.

Capsid damage is usually seen first on headland plants in the vicinity of hedgerows and orchards. Small fields surrounded by high hedges are particularly prone to attack. In many seasons damage is confined to a strip along the headlands: whole fields suffer damage only occasionally.

Although capsid bugs are believed to transmit viruses of potato, conclusive evidence of this is lacking in Britain.

Control

In fields where capsid bugs are known to damage potato crops, attention should be given to general tidying up and destroying weed hosts. There is some evidence that a bare headland left around the crop reduces the incidence of capsid damage.

Chemical control measures are rarely warranted. Phorate or thiofanox granules applied at planting for potato aphid control are also effective in preventing capsid damage.

Further reading

PETHERBRIDGE, F. R. and THORPE, W. H. (1928). The common green capsid bug (*Lygus pabulinus*). *Annals of Applied Biology* **15,** 446–72.

SOUTHWOOD, T. R. E. and LESTON, D. (1959). *Land and Water Bugs of the British Isles*. London: Frederick Warne & Co. Ltd.

WIGHTMAN, J. A. (1967). The hosts and life histories of three mirid bugs of economic importance with notes on their control. *The Entomologist* **100,** 281–3.

Beetles

Beetles comprise a very large group of insects (the Coleoptera) whose front wings are hardened to form a pair of wing-cases. When a beetle is at rest these wing-cases cover the folded hind wings and, in most species, the whole of the abdomen as well. The mouthparts are of the biting type in both the immature and adult stages. Immature beetles (larvae or grubs) are very different in appearance from the adults, so there is a complete metamorphosis with a pupal stage between the young and the adult.

WIREWORMS

Wireworms are the larvae of certain species of click beetles (family Elateridae), so called because of the audible clicking noise made as they flick themselves into the air to right themselves when they fall on to their backs.

Large wireworm populations usually occur only in permanent grassland such as old pasture and leys more than five years old. When this grassland is ploughed in, subsequent arable crops may be damaged. As well as potatoes, cereals and all other root crops are susceptible to attack. In the first year after the grass is ploughed, the wireworms often feed on the decaying turf and may cause relatively little crop damage. However, in the second, third and, occasionally, fourth year after ploughing, wireworms can cause severe crop damage, even at population levels as low as 120 000 per hectare. This level of infestation is difficult to detect by sampling the soil before cropping.

Species

Several species of wireworm attack potato, the commonest being *Agriotes obscurus* (L.), *A. lineatus* (L.) and *A. sputator* (L.). Of these, *A. obscurus* is the most abundant in the northern parts of England and in Scotland, while *A. lineatus* is the dominant species further south. The much larger wireworms belonging to the species *Athous haemorrhoidalis* (L.) also attack potato but are less commonly found than *Agriotes* species.

Description and life history

Adult *Agriotes* species are dull brown, 8–15 mm long and 2–3 mm wide (Plate 6a). The life history and habits of the three *Agriotes* species and *Athous haemorrhoidalis* are very similar.

The life cycle occupies four or five years. The beetles become active in the spring with the advent of warmer weather and each female lays 50–150 eggs in the soil, usually in batches. These eggs hatch after about four weeks and the newly emerged wireworms start to feed on decomposing vegetable matter in the soil. In their first year, wireworms are seldom noticed as they are very small and do little economic damage. From the second year onwards, they are easily recognisable as typical wireworms: yellow, thin and wiry with biting jaws and three pairs of short legs immediately behind the head (Plate 6a). Most wireworms are fully grown after four years, but sometimes five years elapse before they pupate. The pupal stage is spent in an earthen cell, usually at a depth of 75–100 mm but sometimes 300 mm or more, and lasts about four weeks. The newly formed adults emerge in July or August and usually remain in the soil to hibernate, coming to the surface the following spring to lay their eggs. They are active at night, especially in damp weather, and shelter under stones and clods during the day.

Damage

The adults feed on the foliage of grasses and cereals causing only slight damage. The severe crop losses which occur are due entirely to the feeding activities of the larvae; potatoes are particularly liable to serious attack. Wireworms tunnel deeply into the tubers leaving characteristic small round holes on the surface (Plate 6b). This damage does not affect yield but can cause a serious loss of quality resulting in reduced saleability of the crop. Damaged tubers are also predisposed to attack from other pests and diseases. Wireworms usually feed during two distinct periods: the first from March to May and the second during September and October. The newly planted seed can be attacked, the wireworms holing the mother tuber and occasionally the emerging sprout (Fig. 20b). However, the most serious damage usually occurs later in the year when the developing tubers are attacked. Sometimes wireworms tunnel into the pith of the stems, but potato plants are very resistant to wireworm attack and, although the tubers may be riddled by them, the plants are unaffected.

Slugs (see page 56) can cause tuber damage which is superficially similar to wireworm attack. However, slugs usually form an enlarged feeding chamber inside the tuber (Plate 3d) which wireworms do not.

Control

Natural control

Rooks and other birds can be attracted in large numbers to wireworm-infested land but probably only remove a fraction of the total wireworm population. Wireworms are also attacked by some soil insects and fungi. However, in spite of these natural enemies, a balance may be maintained at a population level of wireworms which is still large enough to cause economic damage to subsequent crops.

Cultural control

The control of wireworms by cultural methods cannot be relied on to prevent damage to potatoes grown after grass, mainly because it is almost impossible to reduce the population to a suitably low level. The planting of potatoes in fields known to be infested with wireworms should therefore be avoided. Cultivations (particularly those done in the autumn) help to reduce the wireworm population year by year, the rate of decline depending on the number and type of operations. If an attack develops in an untreated crop, early lifting should be considered because damage increases with the length of time the crop is left in the ground. There are no commercially available potato varieties resistant to wireworm attack.

Since the Second World War ADAS has provided a soil-sampling service to estimate wireworm numbers in grassland to be ploughed. If a field is found to have a population greater than 120 000 wireworms per hectare, potatoes should not be planted.

Chemical control

Chemical control of wireworms was achieved in the late 1950s and early 1960s by the use of fertilisers containing aldrin; when applied in the row before planting, these gave adequate protection against damage. However, this method led to more aldrin being applied than was justifiable and it was discontinued in 1964. Aldrin will be available for use until the early 1990s as a pre-planting spray or dust where potatoes are grown in former pasture. Sprays should be applied in at least 100 litres of water per hectare to open ridges and furrows immediately before planting, or to the soil before ridges are opened, and then worked in with preliminary cultivations. Dusts should be broadcast at least two weeks before planting and worked into the soil. Repeat applications of soil insecticides for wireworm control during the arable part of the rotation should not be necessary.

Aldrin is hazardous to wildlife and adversely affects beneficial insects in the soil. An extensive search has been made for alternative, less harmful insecticides: unfortunately, little progress has been made. Some organophosphorus compounds give partial control of small populations. Ten per cent phorate granules applied in the row at planting will give some control but are less effective against large populations. Phorate may also be less effective when applied to soil containing more than 10 per cent organic matter.

Further reading

ADAS Leaflet 199. *Wireworms*. Ministry of Agriculture, Fisheries and Food, London.

EDWARDS, C. A. and HEATH, G. W. (1964). *The Principles of Agricultural Entomology*. London: Chapman and Hall Ltd.

FRENCH, N. and WHITE, J. H. (1965). Observations on wireworm populations causing damage to ware potatoes. *Plant Pathology* **14,** 41–3.

JONES, F. G. W. and JONES, M. G. (1984). *Pests of Field Crops*. (3rd edition). London: Edward Arnold.

STRICKLAND, A. H., BARDNER, H. M. and WAINES, R. A. (1962). Wireworm damage and insecticidal treatment of the ware potato crop in England and Wales. *Plant Pathology* **11,** 93–105.

CHAFER GRUBS

Chafer grubs are the larvae of chafer beetles, several species of which are crop pests in Britain and continental Europe. The adults occasionally appear in large swarms, especially on the Continent, where they cause severe defoliation of fruit trees, roses, etc. However, in Britain the most serious damage is done by the grubs, which normally live in the soil of grassland.

Species

Three species of chafer can attack potato. These are the cockchafer (*Melolontha melolontha* (L.)), the summer chafer (*Amphimallon solstitialis* (L.)) and the garden chafer (*Phyllopertha horticola* (L.)). Of these, the cockchafer is the species most commonly found attacking potato.

Description and life history

The larvae of these chafers are large, white, fleshy grubs with brown heads and strong biting mandibles (Plate 6c). The body is curved like a sickle and swollen posteriorly with the gut contents showing bluish through the skin.

Adult cockchafers emerge from the soil in May or June and lay their eggs in batches of up to 30 in grassland and occasionally arable fields. The grubs take three years to complete their development, pupating in June–August of the third year. The adults emerge the same year but stay in the pupal cell until the following spring. The garden chafer and the summer chafer normally take one and two years respectively to complete their development.

Damage

The most serious damage usually occurs in grassland, where the roots are severed so that the grass can be pulled out in tufts. Often, the first signs of this damage are birds, such as rooks and jackdaws, pulling out patches of the weakened grass in their search for the grubs. When infested grassland is ploughed, the grubs may damage the ensuing crop. The roots and tubers of potatoes can be attacked (Plate 6c), causing stunted growth.

Control

Attacks by chafer grubs are sporadic and difficult to control because of their subterranean habit. Damage should be avoided whenever possible by not growing potatoes after ploughing grassland if this is seen to be infested. If the crop must be grown in these situations, extra cultivations will reduce the number of chafer grubs: early ploughing followed by discing and rotary tilling are particularly effective. Chafers have some natural enemies: nematode parasites, bacterial diseases and two species of tachinid flies, all of which attack the grubs, while some birds will eat both grubs and adults.

Aldrin applied for the control of wireworms will also control chafer grubs.

Further reading

ADAS Leaflet 235. *Chafer grubs*. Ministry of Agriculture, Fisheries and Food, London.

FIDLER, J. H. (1936). Some notes on the biology and economics of some British chafers. *Annals of Applied Biology* **23**, 409–27.

MILNE, A. (1956). Biology and ecology of the garden chafer, *Phyllopertha horticola* (L.). II. — The cycle from egg to adult in the field. *Bulletin of Entomological Research* **47**, 23–42.

POTATO FLEA BEETLE

The potato flea beetle (*Psylliodes affinis* (Payk.)) is one of the many flea beetles which attack a range of crops. It is 2–3 mm long, yellowish with a dark thigh segment on the hind legs. These legs are enlarged, as in all flea beetles, so that the insect is able to make large jumps, hence the name. The beetles overwinter in plant litter, grass tussocks, hedge bottoms and similar places and emerge to begin feeding in the spring. They feed on the leaves of potato and, if the population is large and the plants are small, considerable 'shot-holing' of the foliage occurs. Once the plants have reached a height of about 30 cm the damage is of little consequence.

Caterpillars of moths

Moths and butterflies together form a large group of insects (the Lepidoptera) whose wings are covered with tiny scales. The young are very different from the adults, being caterpillars with five pairs of fleshy prolegs on the abdomen as well as three pairs of true legs on the thorax. Caterpillars have biting mouthparts, whereas moths and butterflies have a sucking proboscis. There is a complete metamorphosis with a pupal stage between the caterpillar and the adult moth or butterfly.

CUTWORMS

Cutworms are the caterpillars of several moth species belonging to the family Noctuidae (owlet moths). They are called 'cutworms' because of their habit of biting through plant stems at ground level (Fig. 11). Cutworms are most active at night; during the day they lie under clods and stones, curled up on their sides in a characteristic manner.

Description and life history

The caterpillar of the **turnip moth** (*Agrotis segetum* (Schiff.)) is one of the commonest and most damaging cutworms and attacks a wide range of farm and garden plants. Adults emerge from pupae in the soil in late May and June. Eggs are laid on suitable host plants. Initially, the young caterpillars feed on the leaves, but they soon move down into the soil to complete their development. The fully grown caterpillar is about 35 mm long, pale grey or brownish-grey with a pale dark-bordered line along the back and a smoky-brown line along each side (Plate 7a). The caterpillars either overwinter in a cell in the soil or continue to feed, especially during mild weather. They start feeding again more actively in spring and pupate in May or June.

Other cutworms with similar habits and life cycle to the turnip moth caterpillar are sometimes found damaging potato. The caterpillar of the **large yellow underwing moth** (*Noctua pronuba* (L.)) is the commonest of these. It is 40–50 mm long, yellowish-brown or greenish with a line of black streaks bordered by a yellow line along each side. The **garden dart moth** caterpillar (*Euxoa nigricans* (L.)) also occurs commonly and damages potato occasionally. This caterpillar is about 40–50 mm long, pale to dark brown on the back, greenish on the sides, with greyish lines edged with black on the back and a double white line on each side. It feeds from March to June (somewhat earlier than other cutworm species) and is commonest in the Fens and the eastern counties of England.

Damage

Cutworms damage potato by gnawing the roots or the emerging shoots and holing the tubers (Plate 7a); the latter can be fairly severe, if somewhat sporadic, on lighter soils, especially during hot, dry summers. Cutworm damage is often mistaken for damage caused by slugs (see page 56 and Plate 6d). However, slugs usually occur on the heavier, wetter soils and their presence is often indicated by slime trails.

Control

Cultural control

Cutworms are most common on weedy land as it provides cover for the egg-laying moths and food for the caterpillars. Land should therefore be kept as free from weeds as possible. Because young cutworms cannot survive in wet soil, frequent irrigation should also help to prevent the development of damaging infestations. In gardens and allotments, cutworms can be collected by hand at night, when they are active on the soil surface.

Chemical control

Although cutworms are most easily controlled when young, they are seldom noticed until they are well grown and causing obvious damage. Insecticidal sprays are the most effective means of control, particularly if they are applied when the caterpillars are still small and have not yet entered the soil. ADAS Entomologists issue spray warnings for cutworms based on a computer-generated forecast of egg development and caterpillar survival; these should be taken as a guide to the need for, and the correct timing of, treatment.

The insecticides chlorpyrifos and triazophos will give good control of cutworms if applied at the correct time. However, they should not be used if the potato crop is under severe drought stress. Trichlorphon, cypermethrin and alphacypermethrin may also be used. All chemicals should be applied as high-volume drenching sprays in 1100 litres of water per hectare. Methiocarb pellets, when applied for slug control, also give some control of cutworms.

OTHER NOCTUID MOTH CATERPILLARS

There are several other species of noctuid moth which occasionally occur on potato. Although closely related to cutworms, they tend to feed on the aerial parts of the plant and are not usually found in the soil.

The commonest species is the caterpillar of the **rosy rustic moth** (*Hydraecia micacea* (Esp.)), which attacks a wide range of plants including potato, although damage on a field scale is sporadic and rarely serious. The caterpillars hatch from overwintered eggs in the spring and bore into the plant stems near ground level. They tunnel up the stem, hence the popular name of potato stem borer. When fully fed the caterpillar is about 30 mm long, dull flesh-pink, darker on the upper surface, and with lateral wart-like spots each with a blackish bristle. Damage to potato consists in hollowing the stems from the base upwards (Fig. 12); in badly attacked plants, the foliage wilts and finally collapses.

The caterpillar of the closely related **frosted orange moth** (*Gortyna flavago* (Denis & Schiff.)) (Fig. 12) is also occasionally found on potato. Damage by this caterpillar is thought to be more frequent when potatoes follow ploughed grassland.

Caterpillars of two other species of noctuid moth are sometimes found feeding on the haulm of potatoes. These are the **tomato moth** (or bright-line brown-eye moth) caterpillar (*Lacanobia oleracea* (L.)) and the **angle shades moth** caterpillar (*Phlogophora meticulosa* (L.)). The tomato moth caterpillar is about 40 mm long when fully grown, is greenish or yellowish-brown with scattered black and white dots and has a bright yellow line along each side. The fully grown caterpillar of the angle shades moth is about 45–50 mm long, yellowish-green to brown with numerous white spots, a pale dorsal line with a V-shaped mark on either side of it, and a whitish spiracular line along each side of the body. Severe attacks of either species are rare but can result in extensive damage to the leaf margins (Fig. 10) and occasionally complete defoliation.

Control

Because of the sporadic and local nature of infestations of these caterpillars, specific control measures are rarely necessary. Severe attacks could be adequately controlled by the chemicals recommended for cutworm control (see page 85).

Further reading on cutworms and other noctuid moth caterpillars

ADAS Leaflet 225. *Cutworms*. Ministry of Agriculture, Fisheries and Food, London.

JONES, F. G. W. and JONES, M. G. (1984). *Pests of Field Crops*. (3rd edition). London: Edward Arnold.

SHAW, M. W. (1957). Damage by rosy rustic moth larvae in Scotland, 1956. *Plant Pathology* **6,** 135–6.

SOUTH, R. (1961). *The Moths of the British Isles. First Series*. London and New York: Frederick Warne & Co. Ltd.

SWIFT MOTH CATERPILLARS

The caterpillars of two species of swift moth (family Hepialidae) attack potato: these are the ghost swift moth (*Hepialus humuli* (L.)) and the garden swift moth (*H. lupulinus* (L.)). The females of both species lay their eggs while flying over vegetation. The ghost swift moth caterpillar is 35–50 mm long; the body is white with dark tubercles and scattered hairs, whereas the head is red-brown. The garden swift moth caterpillar (Plate 7b) is generally smaller, being 20–35 mm long. The caterpillar of the ghost swift moth takes up to two years to mature, but the garden swift moth usually completes its life cycle in only one year.

Ghost swift moth caterpillars occur mainly in grassland and in land infested with perennial weeds such as couch-grass. Garden swift moth caterpillars are more frequently found in flower beds, where they feed on the roots of herbaceous plants or bulbs. However, they are not uncommon in agricultural land. Both species live underground and do not come to the surface to feed like cutworms. Potatoes are occasionally attacked and the caterpillars eat large cavities in the tubers (Plate 7b), the damage being very similar to that caused by cutworms (see page 84 and Plate 7a).

Control

Owing to their subterranean habit, swift moth caterpillars are difficult to control with insecticides, but their comparative infrequency as pests of potato makes this unnecessary. Cultivation helps to disturb the caterpillars and exposes them to predation by birds. Keeping grassland weed-free also helps to reduce egg laying by the female moths.

Further reading

ADAS Leaflet 160. *Swift moths*. Ministry of Agriculture, Fisheries and Food, London.

EDWARDS, C. A. and DENNIS, E. B. (1960). Observations on the biology and control of the garden swift moth. *Plant Pathology* **9,** 95–9.

DEATH'S HEAD HAWK MOTH CATERPILLAR

The caterpillars of the death's head hawk moth (*Acherontia atropos* (L.)) feed on potato leaves but occur only rarely and should not be regarded as pests. The caterpillar is 125 mm long, as thick as a finger, usually a shade of green or yellowish-brown with purplish-brown diagonal stripes along the side and speckled with white or purple spots. As on most hawk moth caterpillars, there is a short curved 'tail' or 'horn' on the upper, hind end of the body.

Further reading

SOUTH, R. (1961). *The Moths of the British Isles. First Series.* London and New York: Frederick Warne & Co. Ltd.

Other pests

EARWIGS

The common earwig (*Forficula auricularia* L.) eats holes in the leaves of potato but is more commonly found in gardens than in field crops. Earwigs are chestnut-brown insects with elongate bodies, short leathery fore wings meeting in the mid-line and a pair of stout pincers at the end of the abdomen. The young are similar in appearance to the adults. Earwigs feed mainly at night and rest during the day, usually in family groups in soil nests. Sometimes the damage to potato foliage can be quite extensive, but the effect on crop yield is negligible and control measures are uneconomic.

LEATHERJACKETS

Leatherjackets are the grubs of crane flies (daddy longlegs) and occur commonly in grassland. They are about 38mm long when fully grown and are grey, legless and of a fleshy rubbery texture. The adult females of the commonest species, *Tipula paludosa* Meig., lay their eggs in grassland or grassy stubble in August–September. The leatherjackets which emerge from these eggs live through the winter, usually feeding on grass roots. They pupate in the soil in May–June and the adults normally emerge in late summer. Potato may be damaged by leatherjackets when a crop is grown after grassland or after the ploughing of a similar suitable habitat. The shoots growing from the planted seed are sometimes eaten, but damage is usually negligible on a field scale and control measures are not worth while.

Further reading

ADAS Leaflet 179. *Leatherjackets*. Ministry of Agriculture, Fisheries and Food, London.

BIBIONID FLY LARVAE

Larvae of bibionid flies can occasionally damage potatoes grown after grass or on land heavily dressed with farmyard manure. Both the March fly (*Bibio hortulanus* (L.)) and a closely related species (*B. johannis* (L.)) have been reported damaging potato tubers. These small, robust flies are on the wing from March to May and lay their eggs in large clusters in soil containing abundant organic matter, often where dung is present. The legless larvae are often mistaken for small leatherjackets, but they are dark brown and have a definite hard, round head with biting jaws. Although preferring to eat decaying plant material and other organic debris, the larvae may feed on potato tubers in July and August, causing superficial pitting similar to the early stage of wireworm attack. Damage is unlikely to be serious on a field scale and control measures are unnecessary.

ANTS

Very occasionally potatoes are reported to be damaged by ants. Damage is usually confined to small gardens and is rarely found in the field where it might be confused with a severe wireworm attack. The damage takes the form of a pitting on the surface of the tubers during July and August (Plate 7c). The mound ant (*Lasius flavus* (F.)) has been shown experimentally to produce such damage. It might be reasonable to implicate ants if this kind of damage is found either in the field or in clamps and is not attributable to wireworms or 'pit-rot'.

Further reading

WESTON, W. A. R. DILLON (1953). Injury to potato tubers by ants. *Plant Pathology* **2,** 55–6.

SYMPHYLIDS

Potato is sometimes attacked by the glasshouse symphylid (*Scutigerella immaculata*) (Newp.)), but damage on a field scale is rare. Symphylids are not insects but are closely related to millepedes and centipedes. They are white, about 6 mm long, with 12 pairs of legs, long antennae and appendages called cerci on the posterior segment of the body (Fig. 2b, inset). The glasshouse symphylid takes at least three months to complete its life cycle, may live for two years or more and feeds throughout the year even outdoors. Symphylids are very active but are seldom seen as they live in cracks in the soil several centimetres below the surface. Damage to potato takes the form of dark brown lesions on the roots (Fig. 2b) and grazing of the root hairs; in severe attacks the plants may wilt. Entry into the wound by fungi often accentuates the damage.

Control

Some granular insecticides (e.g. carbofuran) applied at planting as aphicides or nematicides may reduce the likelihood of symphylid attack, but no chemical control is completely effective.

Further reading

ADAS Leaflet 484. *Symphylids.* Ministry of Agriculture, Fisheries and Food, London.

EDWARDS, C. A. (1958). The ecology of Symphyla. Part I. Populations. *Entomologia Experimentalis et Applicata* **1,** 308–19.

EDWARDS, C. A. (1959). The ecology of Symphyla. Part II. Seasonal soil migrations. *Entomologia Experimentalis et Applicata* **2,** 257–67.

EDWARDS, C. A. (1961). The ecology of Symphyla. Part III. Factors controlling soil distributions. *Entomologia Experimentalis et Applicata* **4,** 239–56.

MILLEPEDES

Millepedes are very common in many fields but are most numerous on the heavier wetter soils, especially where these have a large organic content as a result of heavy farmyard manuring or the ploughing-in of straw. Millepedes are not insects but are related to centipedes, with which they should not be confused. Millepedes differ from centipedes in having two pairs of legs on each segment and in being relatively slow moving and vegetarian, rather than very active and carnivorous.

The most important millepedes attacking potato are the spotted millepede (*Blaniulus guttulatus* (Bosc)), one species of black millepede (*Cylindroiulus londinensis* (Leach)) and both species of flat millepede (*Polydesmus angustus* Latz. and *Brachydesmus superus* Latz.). The spotted millepede has an almost cylindrical body, which is about 8–20 mm long and pale straw-coloured with a row of red spots along each side (Plate 7d). The black millepede species has a cylindrical body, which is 20–50 mm long and black. *Polydesmus angustus* has a flattened body, which is 20–25 mm long and pale purplish-white to red-brown. *Brachydesmus superus* is similar to the previous species but is shorter, 8–10 mm long, and pale brown.

Millepedes occur somewhat sporadically on a field scale and are usually found sheltering and feeding in holes on tubers already attacked by other pests such as slugs or wireworms (Plate 7d). As the millepedes extend this damage large numbers can be found associated with the resultant rotting tissue. When abundant they act as primary feeders, scarring the surface of the tuber or tunnelling into the flesh forming shallow cavities.

Control

Because of their subterranean habit and the unpredictability of attack, control of millepedes in potato crops is very difficult. The use of prophylactic granular pesticides, applied in the furrow at planting against soil pests and aphids, will give some control of millepedes but is not worth while against them alone.

Further reading

ADAS Leaflet 150. *Millepedes and centipedes.* Ministry of Agriculture, Fisheries and Food, London.

BLOWER, J. G. (1958). British Millipedes (Diplopoda). With keys to the species. *The Linnean Society of London Synopses of the British Fauna* No. 11.

WOODLICE

Woodlice of the species *Armadillidium* have occasionally been found damaging potato. Woodlice are crustaceans and are therefore more closely related to crabs and lobsters than to insects or millepedes. They have an oval-shaped body with seven pairs of legs. They damage potatoes by eating the shoots and tubers, especially where the latter have been damaged already by slugs or wireworms.

Control

Where necessary, control can be achieved by trapping or by the use of methiocarb pellets.

Further reading

ADAS Leaflet 623. *Woodlice.* Ministry of Agriculture, Fisheries and Food, London.

SUTTON, S. (1980). *Woodlice.* Oxford: Pergamon Press.

Foreign pests

Several hundred species of insect which are not found in Britain attack potatoes in other countries, but it is surprising how few insect pests appear to have been brought with the potato from its original home in the Andes of South America. The potato is now grown world-wide and the majority of its pests are indigenous species that have moved from other hosts on to potato when the opportunity arose. For a few of these species the potato was so favourable a host that they were able to spread (either by natural means or with the aid of man) far beyond the bounds of their original ranges.

SUCKING INSECTS

Because they are so easily dispersed by air currents and because it often needs only one individual to found a colony, the main potato aphid species are now practically cosmopolitan. Leafhoppers are also readily transported by wind, but as their reproduction is usually bisexual they do not colonise new areas as readily as do aphids. Thus the American leafhoppers *Empoasca fabae* (Harris), *E. filamenta* (Delong) and *Macrosteles fascifrons* (Stål) have not yet spread to Britain. Although many of these insects which suck the potato sap can cause some direct damage to the plant, they also transmit viruses that cause disease. There are several potato viruses, particularly in South America, which are not found in Britain.

LEAF-EATING INSECTS

Colorado beetle

Pests that feed only on the foliage of potato seldom cause much loss of yield in cool, temperate regions unless they also transmit diseases. However, one pest that can cause considerable damage is the notorious Colorado beetle (*Leptinotarsa decemlineata* (Say)). Both the adults and larvae feed on potato leaves and can defoliate and kill a potato crop. Such extreme damage is normally seen only in continental conditions of N. America or Europe when the hot sunshine favours the rapid multiplication of the beetle and when the growth of the plants is checked by water deficiency.

The Colorado beetle appears to have evolved as a local species feeding on wild *Solanum rostratum* along the eastern slopes of the Rocky Mountains in the USA. This area was bounded to the east by a zone where the food plant was absent. When the cultivated potato was introduced, beetles transferred to this new food plant and then dispersed from their original habitat. The main spread occurred during the latter half of the 19th century and, by 1900, Colorado beetle had become a serious pest throughout the USA and southern Canada. It has since spread across most of Europe from an introduction near Bordeaux about 1921.

The first outbreak in England occurred in 1901 and since then many breeding colonies have been found, mostly between 1945 and 1952 and again in 1976–77. All these colonies were exterminated. The Channel is probably an effective barrier to direct flight of beetles from the Continent, although in 1950 some of the colonies along the south coast may have been started by beetles washed ashore. Beetles have been seen floating in the sea and are often found on beaches in the Channel Islands.

In Britain almost all the beetles found are associated with transport or with imported goods. Beetles are most commonly found on ships, aircraft and road vehicles from May to September. These are the months when adult beetles are flying most actively and may land on vehicles and remain there until the vehicles reach Britain. Some of the largest finds of the Colorado beetle have been on ships that have loaded at Mediterranean ports.

Legislation was introduced as long ago as 1877 to restrict the import of produce likely to carry Colorado beetle; this legislation has undoubtedly been effective in reducing the numbers of this pest reaching Britain. Most beetles have been found with potatoes or salad vegetables. Celery, endive, parsley and spinach seem to provide harbourage for beetles, especially during the winter and spring, and they can survive prolonged chilling at 0°C in refrigerated transport and stores. Large numbers of them have also been found in timber imported during the summer and in grain imported in the autumn.

There are no insects feeding on potato leaves in Britain that resemble the black and yellow striped adults (Plate 8c) or the carrot-red larvae (Plate 8b) of Colorado beetle.

The beetles spend the winter buried in the soil and, in north-west Europe, emerge from May through to early June. In warm and sunny weather they fly actively. When they find a potato crop the beetles feed on the leaves and the females lay batches of orange-yellow eggs (Plate 8a), usually on the underside of the lower leaves. The beetles are long-lived and the females may continue to lay batches of eggs throughout the summer.

The eggs hatch in one to two weeks and the larvae, at first brownish with a black head, feed on the leaves. As they grow, the larvae become bright carrot-red with two rows of black dots along each side. When fully grown, usually three to five weeks after hatching, the larvae burrow into the soil to pupate. The pupae remain in the soil for two to three weeks until the adult beetles emerge towards the end of July and early August. In a hot summer there may be another generation before the autumn.

The Plant Health (Great Britain) Order 1987, which replaces the previous Colorado Beetle Orders, requires occupiers of land to report to the Ministry of Agriculture, Fisheries and Food any suspected outbreak of Colorado beetle. When a breeding colony is discovered, the Ministry takes immediate action to eradicate it. Suspected beetles or larvae found in England or Wales should be placed in a strong box or tin and sent or taken to the nearest office of the Ministry of Agriculture, Fisheries and Food. Those found in Scotland should be sent to the Department of Agriculture and Fisheries for Scotland in Edinburgh. The keeping of live Colorado beetle is prohibited.

Further reading

ADAS Leaflet 71. *Colorado beetle (A crop pest not yet established in Britain)*. Ministry of Agriculture, Fisheries and Food, London.

BARTLETT, P. W. (1979). Preventing the establishment of Colorado beetle in England and Wales. In EBBELS, D. L. and KING, J. E. (Eds) *Plant Health. The Scientific Basis for Administrative Control of Plant Diseases and Pests*. pp. 247–57. Oxford: Blackwell Scientific Publications.

BARTLETT, P. W. (1980). Interception and eradication of Colorado beetle in England and Wales, 1958–1977. *EPPO Bulletin* **10,** 481–9.

BARTLETT, P. W. (1983). Interception of Colorado beetle in England and Wales, 1978–1982. *EPPO Bulletin* **13,** 559–62.

GIBSON, R. W. (1978). Pest aspects of potato production. Part 2. Pests other than nematodes. In HARRIS, P. M. (Ed.) *The Potato Crop. The Scientific Basis for Improvement*. pp. 470–503. London: Chapman & Hall.

THOMAS, G. and WOOD, F. (1980). Colorado beetle in the Channel Islands. *EPPO Bulletin* **10,** 491–8.

Ladybird beetles

In many countries potato haulm is damaged by ladybird beetles belonging to the genus *Epilachna*. Species of *Epilachna* occur in many of the warmer parts of the world but are unlikely to become pests outdoors in Britain.

LEAF MINERS

In some parts of the world agromyzid leaf miners are serious pests of potato. The larvae of these flies tunnel within the leaves, making yellowish mines whose pattern is often diagnostic of the species responsible. The species *Liriomyza trifolii* (Burgess) and *L. huidobrensis* (Blanchard) have been reported damaging potato in the Americas.

TUBER PESTS

Because the tubers are the marketable product of the potato crop, damage to them can result in serious losses due to downgrading or the introduction of storage rots. Wireworms, chafers and cutworms are cosmopolitan groups although the pest species differ in different parts of the world. Many of these alien species from cool, temperate regions could probably survive if introduced into Britain, but how they would perform in competition with our native species is impossible to predict.

American potato flea beetles

Foremost among the alien species for potential establishment in Britain must be the potato flea beetles of North America, *Epitrix tuberis* Gentner, *E. cucumeris* (Harris) and *E.*

subcrinita (Le Conte). Unlike our own potato flea beetle (see page 83) the larvae of these *Epitrix* species regularly feed on and in the potato tubers. In British Columbia in areas climatically very similar to Britain, the larvae of *E. tuberis* can cause severe damage to potato crops where control measures are inadequate.

Andean potato weevils

The larvae of another group of beetles cause severe damage to potato crops in the high Andes of South America. These are the potato weevils *Premnotrypes latithorax* (Pierce), *P. vorax* (Hustache), *P. solani* Pierce and several other species. These pests are thought to have been spread to previously uninfested areas in South America by the planting of infested tubers; larvae have been found alive in tubers imported into the USA from South America. Although it seems unlikely that these weevils would adapt readily to the British climate, so different from their native montane environment, such adaptation is not impossible and is one reason for the long-standing restrictions on the import of potato tubers from South America.

Potato tuber moth

One species of moth whose caterpillars damage potato tubers is regularly imported into Britain. This is the potato tuber moth (*Phthorimaea operculella* (Zell.)), which appears to have originated in America but is now almost cosmopolitan. Where adequate control measures are not taken, this species is a serious pest of potatoes, especially in store. It can also attack tomato, tobacco and other Solanaceae.

Damage to potatoes seems to be most severe in soils which readily crack, as the female moths can then easily reach the tubers on which to lay their eggs. If potatoes are left exposed in the field at lifting when moths are about, eggs are laid on them and stores become reinfested. The species can maintain itself by mining in potato haulm, but this rarely causes serious damage.

In the warmer regions of its geographical range, potato tuber moth can reproduce continuously in potatoes in store. There is no diapause and it overwinters in all stages of development. At high temperatures the life cycle is completed in only a month and six or more generations are sometimes completed in a year. The eggs are laid in leaf axils, around the eyes of tubers, and in similar crevices. The caterpillars mine in the tubers, stems and leaves. When they become too large to mine within the leaves, the caterpillars may fold leaves or spin them together and feed externally. Pupation takes place in a cocoon among dead leaves, on the surface of soil or on tubers, or on the sacks or boxes in which potatoes are packed. The caterpillars incorporate particles from their surroundings into the cocoons, which often makes them difficult to find.

It seems most unlikely that potato tuber moth could survive outdoors in Britain except in a few very sheltered sites on the south coast of England. It has been found in potato stores and might just maintain itself in these, but well managed stores are kept too cool to allow it to build up to sufficient numbers to become a serious pest. Glasshouse tomatoes seem to be the only crop that tuber moth might damage in Britain but it could probably be eliminated from isolated glasshouses without difficulty.

Root-lesion nematodes

In the warmer parts of the USA, a root-lesion nematode, *Pratylenchus scribneri* Steiner, attacks potato tubers, causing small depressed lesions on the skin, each with a slightly raised eruption or pustule in the centre where the nematodes may be found. The characteristic symptoms are caused when the pest penetrates the lenticels.

Another species, *P. brachyurus* (Godfrey) Filipjev & Sch. Stek., causes very similar injury to potato tubers in South Africa and Brazil. In South Africa this species is called the 'potato skin eelworm' and is a serious pest in the Transvaal Highveld. Because of the risk of nematode spread infested tubers are unsaleable as seed and their value as ware is much reduced. Although the damage is superficial, the tubers are rendered more liable to secondary infections and storage rots. *P. brachyurus* has a wide host range so populations are maintained in the soil by other crops.

Neither *P. scribneri* nor *P. brachyurus* is known to occur in Britain but they might be found on imported potatoes. The damage superficially resembles that caused by the fungus disease skin spot (*Oospora pustulans*) with which it might be confused.

Further reading

COMMONWEALTH INSTITUTE OF HELMINTHOLOGY. *Pratylenchus scribneri.* Descriptions of plant-parasitic nematodes, Set 8, No. 110.

COMMONWEALTH INSTITUTE OF HELMINTHOLOGY. *Pratylenchus brachyurus.* Descriptions of plant-parasitic nematodes, Set 6, No. 89.

Root-knot nematodes

Only a few of the many species of root-knot nematodes (*Meloidogyne* spp.) can survive the British climate outdoors, but several others occur as glasshouse pests. In tropical and sub-tropical regions, however, they are serious pests of many important field crops including potatoes; hence they are sometimes found in imported potatoes, e.g. from the Canary Islands and Mediterranean countries.

Infested tubers are not always easy to detect. They show slight swellings and irregularities on the surface that may be almost unnoticeable unless the infestation is fairly severe. On cutting the tubers, the female root-knot nematodes may be seen as tiny white spots, generally fairly near the surface and below the swellings. A hand lens is a help in detecting them, although they are usually made more conspicuous by a thin ring of brown tissue round each female, which is further surrounded by a faint halo of translucent tissue where the starch has been depleted from the adjacent cells. Severe infestations may render an affected consignment unsaleable for ware. Imported potatoes are unlikely to be used for seed but, if by chance infested tubers were planted, the nematodes might spread into that season's crop. However, they would be unlikely to persist in the field for more than one season under British conditions.

ROOT PESTS

False root-knot nematodes

False root-knot nematodes (*Nacobbus* spp.) are gall-forming, endoparasites of plant roots occurring chiefly in western states of the USA and Latin America, but reported also in India and under glass in Europe and the USSR. The only two European reports have been on tomatoes in England (1959) and in glasshouse soil in the Netherlands (1968).

During the 1970s *Nacobbus aberrans* (Thorne) Thorne & Allen was found to be a very damaging pest of potatoes in Argentina, Bolivia, Ecuador and Peru, often occurring with potato cyst nematodes. Most potato fields in southern Peru and Bolivia are severely infested and, in these areas, *N. aberrans* ranks as one of the three most important nematode pests, the others being potato cyst nematodes and root-knot nematodes.

The soil in the infested Andean areas is regularly subjected to freezing and drying and at present there is every reason to assume that this pest could survive in northern Europe. The prohibition, in British import regulations since 1980, of either soil with plant material from South America or seed potatoes from South America should help to safeguard against, or at least delay, introduction of this pest.

Further reading

COMMONWEALTH INSTITUTE OF HELMINTHOLOGY. *Nacobbus aberrans*. Descriptions of plant-parasitic nematodes, Set 8, No. 119.

Precautions

Whenever pesticides are used, read and follow carefully the instructions on the label. Users should also consult Booklet 2272, *Guidelines for applying crop protection chemicals*. Use pesticides with care* and wash off any chemical that falls on the skin. Dazomet, dichloropropene and metham-sodium are strongly irritating to the skin, eyes and respiratory system. Store new and partly used containers in a safe place under lock and key (see Leaflet 767, *Farm chemical stores*). Wash out empty containers thoroughly and dispose of them safely. Do not contaminate ponds, ditches or waterways with concentrate, dip solution, washings or used containers (see Booklet 2198, *Guidelines for the disposal of unwanted pesticides and containers on farms and holdings*). Alphacypermethrin, cypermethrin and deltamethrin are extremely dangerous to fish. Metaldehyde is dangerous to livestock, game and wildlife.

---

*There are statutory obligations affecting employers and workers who use certain poisonous substances, including aldicarb, alphacypermethrin, carbofuran, deltamethrin, demeton-S-methyl, disulfoton, oxamyl, oxydemeton-methyl, phorate, thiofanox, thiometon and triazophos. Users of these chemicals are strongly advised to read Leaflet HS(G)2, *Poisonous chemicals on the farm*, obtainable from the local offices of the Health and Safety Executive.

Index

Printed in the United Kingdom for Her Majesty's Stationery Office
289481 C30 5/89 3936 12521